www.EffortlessMath.com

... So Much More Online!

✓ FREE Math lessons

✓ More Math learning books!

✓ Mathematics Worksheets

✓ Online Math Tutors

Need a PDF version of this book?

Please visit www.EffortlessMath.com

Comprehensive SSAT Middle Level Math Practice Book 2020 - 2021

Complete Coverage of all SSAT Middle Level Math Concepts + 2 Full-Length SSAT Middle Level Math Tests

By

Reza Nazari & Ava Ross

ISBN: 978-1-64612-354-4

Published by: Effortless Math Education

www.EffortlessMath.com

Visit www.EffortlessMath.com

for Online Math Practice

Description

Comprehensive SSAT Middle Level Math Practice Book 2020 - 2021, which reflects the 2020 - 2021 test guidelines, is a precious learning resource for SSAT Middle Level test-takers who need extra practice in math to raise their SSAT Middle Level Math scores. Upon completion of this exercise book, you will have a solid foundation and sufficient practice to ace the SSAT Middle Level Math test. **This comprehensive practice book is your ticket to scoring higher on SSAT Middle Level Math.**

The updated version of this unique practice workbook represents extensive exercises, math problems, sample SSAT Middle Level questions, and quizzes with answers and detailed solutions to help you hone your math skills, overcome your exam anxiety, boost your confidence—and do your best to defeat the SSAT Middle Level exam on test day.

Comprehensive SSAT Middle Level Math Practice Book 2020 – 2021 includes many exciting and unique features to help you improve your test scores, including:

- ✓ Content 100% aligned with the 2020 SSAT Middle Level® test
- ✓ Complete coverage of all SSAT Middle Level Math concepts and topics which you will be tested
- ✓ Over 2,500 additional SSAT Middle Level math practice questions in both multiple-choice and grid-in formats with answers grouped by topic, so you can focus on your weak areas
- ✓ Abundant Math skill-building exercises to help test-takers approach different question types that might be unfamiliar to them
- ✓ 2 full-length practice tests (featuring new question types) with detailed answers

This SSAT Middle Level Math practice book and other Effortless Math Education books are used by thousands of students each year to help them review core content areas, brush-up in math, discover their strengths and weaknesses, and achieve their best scores on the SSAT Middle Level test.

Contents

Chapter 1:

Fractions and Mixed Numbers

Math Topics that you'll learn in this Chapter:

- ✓ Simplifying Fractions

- ✓ Adding and Subtracting Fractions

- ✓ Multiplying and Dividing Fractions

- ✓ Adding Mixed Numbers

- ✓ Subtracting Mixed Numbers

- ✓ Multiplying Mixed Numbers

- ✓ Dividing Mixed Numbers

Simplifying Fractions

✎ *Simplify each fraction.*

1) $\frac{10}{15} =$

2) $\frac{8}{20} =$

3) $\frac{12}{42} =$

4) $\frac{5}{20} =$

5) $\frac{6}{18} =$

6) $\frac{18}{27} =$

7) $\frac{15}{55} =$

8) $\frac{24}{54} =$

9) $\frac{63}{72} =$

10) $\frac{40}{64} =$

11) $\frac{23}{46} =$

12) $\frac{35}{63} =$

13) $\frac{32}{36} =$

14) $\frac{81}{99} =$

15) $\frac{16}{64} =$

16) $\frac{14}{35} =$

17) $\frac{19}{38} =$

18) $\frac{18}{54} =$

19) $\frac{56}{70} =$

20) $\frac{40}{45} =$

21) $\frac{9}{90} =$

22) $\frac{20}{25} =$

23) $\frac{32}{48} =$

24) $\frac{7}{49} =$

25) $\frac{18}{48} =$

26) $\frac{54}{108} =$

Adding and Subtracting Fractions

✎ *Calculate and write the answer in lowest term.*

1) $\frac{1}{5} + \frac{1}{7} =$

2) $\frac{3}{7} + \frac{4}{5} =$

3) $\frac{3}{8} - \frac{1}{9} =$

4) $\frac{4}{5} - \frac{5}{9} =$

5) $\frac{2}{9} + \frac{1}{3} =$

6) $\frac{3}{10} + \frac{2}{5} =$

7) $\frac{9}{10} - \frac{4}{5} =$

8) $\frac{7}{9} - \frac{3}{7} =$

9) $\frac{3}{4} + \frac{1}{3} =$

10) $\frac{3}{8} + \frac{2}{5} =$

11) $\frac{3}{4} - \frac{2}{5} =$

12) $\frac{7}{9} - \frac{2}{3} =$

13) $\frac{4}{9} + \frac{5}{6} =$

14) $\frac{2}{3} + \frac{1}{4} =$

15) $\frac{9}{10} - \frac{3}{5} =$

16) $\frac{7}{12} - \frac{1}{2} =$

17) $\frac{4}{5} + \frac{2}{3} =$

18) $\frac{5}{7} + \frac{1}{5} =$

19) $\frac{5}{9} - \frac{2}{5} =$

20) $\frac{3}{5} - \frac{2}{9} =$

21) $\frac{7}{9} + \frac{1}{7} =$

22) $\frac{5}{8} + \frac{2}{3} =$

23) $\frac{4}{7} + \frac{2}{3} =$

24) $\frac{6}{7} - \frac{4}{9} =$

25) $\frac{4}{5} - \frac{2}{15} =$

26) $\frac{2}{9} + \frac{4}{5} =$

Multiplying and Dividing Fractions

✎ *Solve and write the answer in lowest term.*

1) $\frac{1}{2} \times \frac{4}{5} =$

2) $\frac{1}{5} \times \frac{6}{7} =$

3) $\frac{1}{3} \div \frac{1}{7} =$

4) $\frac{1}{7} \div \frac{3}{8} =$

5) $\frac{2}{3} \times \frac{4}{7} =$

6) $\frac{5}{7} \times \frac{3}{4} =$

7) $\frac{2}{5} \div \frac{3}{7} =$

8) $\frac{3}{7} \div \frac{5}{8} =$

9) $\frac{3}{8} \times \frac{4}{7} =$

10) $\frac{2}{9} \times \frac{6}{11} =$

11) $\frac{1}{10} \div \frac{3}{8} =$

12) $\frac{3}{10} \div \frac{4}{5} =$

13) $\frac{6}{7} \times \frac{4}{9} =$

14) $\frac{3}{7} \times \frac{5}{6} =$

15) $\frac{7}{9} \div \frac{6}{11} =$

16) $\frac{1}{15} \div \frac{2}{3} =$

17) $\frac{1}{13} \times \frac{1}{2} =$

18) $\frac{1}{12} \times \frac{4}{7} =$

19) $\frac{1}{15} \div \frac{4}{9} =$

20) $\frac{1}{16} \div \frac{1}{2} =$

21) $\frac{4}{7} \times \frac{5}{8} =$

22) $\frac{1}{11} \times \frac{4}{5} =$

23) $\frac{1}{18} \div \frac{5}{6} =$

24) $\frac{1}{15} \div \frac{3}{8} =$

25) $\frac{1}{11} \times \frac{3}{4} =$

26) $\frac{1}{14} \times \frac{2}{3} =$

Adding Mixed Numbers

🖎 *Solve and write the answer in lowest terms.*

1) $3\frac{1}{5} + 2\frac{2}{9} =$

2) $1\frac{1}{7} + 5\frac{2}{5} =$

3) $4\frac{4}{5} + 1\frac{2}{7} =$

4) $2\frac{4}{7} + 2\frac{3}{5} =$

5) $1\frac{5}{6} + 1\frac{2}{5} =$

6) $3\frac{5}{7} + 1\frac{2}{9} =$

7) $3\frac{5}{8} + 2\frac{1}{3} =$

8) $1\frac{6}{7} + 3\frac{2}{9} =$

9) $2\frac{5}{9} + 1\frac{1}{4} =$

10) $3\frac{7}{9} + 2\frac{5}{6} =$

11) $2\frac{1}{10} + 2\frac{2}{5} =$

12) $1\frac{3}{10} + 3\frac{4}{5} =$

13) $3\frac{1}{12} + 2\frac{1}{3} =$

14) $5\frac{1}{11} + 1\frac{1}{2} =$

15) $3\frac{1}{21} + 2\frac{2}{3} =$

16) $4\frac{1}{24} + 1\frac{5}{8} =$

17) $2\frac{1}{25} + 3\frac{3}{5} =$

18) $3\frac{1}{15} + 2\frac{2}{10} =$

19) $5\frac{6}{7} + 2\frac{1}{3} =$

20) $2\frac{1}{8} + 3\frac{3}{4} =$

21) $2\frac{5}{7} + 2\frac{2}{21} =$

22) $4\frac{1}{6} + 1\frac{4}{5} =$

23) $3\frac{5}{6} + 1\frac{2}{7} =$

24) $2\frac{7}{8} + 3\frac{1}{3} =$

25) $3\frac{1}{17} + 1\frac{1}{2} =$

26) $1\frac{1}{18} + 1\frac{4}{9} =$

Subtracting Mixed Numbers

✍ *Solve and write the answer in lowest terms.*

1) $3\frac{2}{5} - 1\frac{2}{9} =$

2) $5\frac{3}{5} - 1\frac{1}{7} =$

3) $4\frac{2}{5} - 2\frac{2}{7} =$

4) $8\frac{3}{4} - 2\frac{1}{8} =$

5) $9\frac{5}{7} - 7\frac{4}{21} =$

6) $11\frac{7}{12} - 9\frac{5}{6} =$

7) $9\frac{5}{9} - 8\frac{1}{8} =$

8) $13\frac{7}{9} - 11\frac{3}{7} =$

9) $8\frac{7}{12} - 7\frac{3}{8} =$

10) $11\frac{5}{9} - 9\frac{1}{4} =$

11) $6\frac{5}{6} - 2\frac{2}{9} =$

12) $5\frac{7}{8} - 4\frac{1}{3} =$

13) $9\frac{5}{8} - 8\frac{1}{2} =$

14) $4\frac{9}{16} - 2\frac{1}{4} =$

15) $3\frac{2}{3} - 1\frac{2}{15} =$

16) $5\frac{1}{2} - 4\frac{2}{17} =$

17) $5\frac{6}{7} - 2\frac{1}{3} =$

18) $3\frac{3}{7} - 2\frac{2}{21} =$

19) $7\frac{3}{10} - 5\frac{2}{15} =$

20) $4\frac{5}{6} - 2\frac{2}{9} =$

21) $6\frac{3}{7} - 2\frac{2}{9} =$

22) $7\frac{4}{5} - 6\frac{3}{7} =$

23) $10\frac{2}{3} - 9\frac{5}{8} =$

24) $9\frac{3}{4} - 7\frac{4}{9} =$

25) $15\frac{4}{5} - 13\frac{12}{25} =$

26) $13\frac{5}{12} - 7\frac{5}{24} =$

Multiplying Mixed Numbers

✎ *Solve and write the answer in lowest terms.*

1) $1\frac{1}{8} \times 1\frac{3}{4} =$

2) $3\frac{1}{5} \times 2\frac{2}{7} =$

3) $2\frac{1}{8} \times 1\frac{2}{9} =$

4) $2\frac{3}{8} \times 2\frac{2}{5} =$

5) $1\frac{1}{2} \times 5\frac{2}{3} =$

6) $3\frac{1}{2} \times 6\frac{2}{3} =$

7) $9\frac{1}{2} \times 2\frac{1}{6} =$

8) $2\frac{5}{8} \times 8\frac{3}{5} =$

9) $3\frac{4}{5} \times 4\frac{2}{3} =$

10) $5\frac{1}{3} \times 2\frac{2}{7} =$

11) $6\frac{1}{3} \times 3\frac{3}{4} =$

12) $7\frac{2}{3} \times 1\frac{8}{9} =$

13) $8\frac{1}{2} \times 2\frac{1}{6} =$

14) $4\frac{1}{5} \times 8\frac{2}{3} =$

15) $3\frac{1}{8} \times 5\frac{2}{3} =$

16) $2\frac{2}{7} \times 6\frac{2}{5} =$

17) $2\frac{3}{8} \times 7\frac{2}{3} =$

18) $1\frac{7}{8} \times 8\frac{2}{3} =$

19) $9\frac{1}{2} \times 3\frac{1}{5} =$

20) $2\frac{5}{8} \times 4\frac{1}{3} =$

21) $6\frac{1}{3} \times 3\frac{2}{5} =$

22) $5\frac{3}{4} \times 2\frac{2}{7} =$

23) $9\frac{1}{4} \times 2\frac{1}{3} =$

24) $3\frac{3}{7} \times 7\frac{2}{5} =$

25) $4\frac{1}{4} \times 3\frac{2}{5} =$

26) $7\frac{2}{3} \times 3\frac{2}{5} =$

Dividing Mixed Numbers

✍ *Solve and write the answer in lowest terms.*

1) $9\frac{1}{2} \div 2\frac{3}{5} =$

2) $2\frac{3}{8} \div 1\frac{2}{5} =$

3) $5\frac{3}{4} \div 2\frac{2}{7} =$

4) $8\frac{1}{3} \div 4\frac{1}{4} =$

5) $7\frac{2}{5} \div 3\frac{3}{4} =$

6) $2\frac{4}{5} \div 3\frac{2}{3} =$

7) $8\frac{3}{5} \div 4\frac{3}{4} =$

8) $6\frac{3}{4} \div 2\frac{2}{9} =$

9) $5\frac{2}{7} \div 2\frac{2}{9} =$

10) $2\frac{2}{5} \div 3\frac{3}{5} =$

11) $4\frac{3}{7} \div 1\frac{7}{8} =$

12) $2\frac{5}{7} \div 2\frac{4}{5} =$

13) $8\frac{3}{5} \div 6\frac{1}{5} =$

14) $2\frac{5}{8} \div 1\frac{8}{9} =$

15) $5\frac{6}{7} \div 2\frac{3}{4} =$

16) $1\frac{3}{5} \div 2\frac{3}{8} =$

17) $5\frac{3}{4} \div 3\frac{2}{5} =$

18) $2\frac{3}{4} \div 3\frac{1}{5} =$

19) $3\frac{2}{3} \div 1\frac{2}{5} =$

20) $4\frac{1}{4} \div 2\frac{2}{3} =$

21) $3\frac{5}{6} \div 2\frac{4}{5} =$

22) $2\frac{1}{8} \div 1\frac{3}{4} =$

23) $5\frac{1}{2} \div 2\frac{2}{5} =$

24) $3\frac{4}{7} \div 2\frac{2}{3} =$

25) $2\frac{4}{5} \div 3\frac{5}{6} =$

26) $2\frac{3}{7} \div 3\frac{2}{3} =$

Answers – Chapter 1

Simplifying Fractions

1) $\frac{2}{3}$

2) $\frac{2}{5}$

3) $\frac{2}{7}$

4) $\frac{1}{4}$

5) $\frac{1}{3}$

6) $\frac{2}{3}$

7) $\frac{3}{11}$

8) $\frac{4}{9}$

9) $\frac{7}{8}$

10) $\frac{5}{8}$

11) $\frac{1}{2}$

12) $\frac{5}{9}$

13) $\frac{8}{9}$

14) $\frac{9}{11}$

15) $\frac{1}{4}$

16) $\frac{2}{5}$

17) $\frac{1}{2}$

18) $\frac{1}{3}$

19) $\frac{4}{5}$

20) $\frac{8}{9}$

21) $\frac{1}{10}$

22) $\frac{4}{5}$

23) $\frac{2}{3}$

24) $\frac{1}{7}$

25) $\frac{3}{8}$

26) $\frac{1}{2}$

Adding and Subtracting Fractions

1) $\frac{12}{35}$

2) $\frac{43}{35}$

3) $\frac{19}{72}$

4) $\frac{11}{45}$

5) $\frac{5}{9}$

6) $\frac{7}{10}$

25) $\frac{2}{3}$

7) $\frac{1}{10}$

8) $\frac{22}{63}$

9) $\frac{13}{12}$

10) $\frac{31}{40}$

11) $\frac{7}{20}$

12) $\frac{1}{9}$

26) $\frac{46}{45}$

13) $\frac{23}{18}$

14) $\frac{11}{12}$

15) $\frac{3}{10}$

16) $\frac{1}{12}$

17) $\frac{22}{15}$

18) $\frac{32}{35}$

19) $\frac{7}{45}$

20) $\frac{17}{45}$

21) $\frac{58}{63}$

22) $\frac{31}{24}$

23) $\frac{26}{21}$

24) $\frac{26}{63}$

Multiplying and Dividing Fractions

1) $\frac{2}{5}$

2) $\frac{6}{35}$

3) $\frac{7}{3}$

4) $\frac{8}{21}$

5) $\frac{8}{21}$

6) $\frac{15}{28}$

7) $\frac{14}{15}$

8) $\frac{24}{35}$

9) $\frac{3}{14}$

10) $\frac{4}{33}$

11) $\frac{4}{15}$

12) $\frac{3}{8}$

13) $\frac{8}{21}$

14) $\frac{5}{14}$

15) $\frac{77}{54}$

16) $\frac{1}{10}$

17) $\frac{1}{26}$

18) $\frac{1}{21}$

19) $\frac{3}{20}$

20) $\frac{1}{8}$

21) $\frac{5}{14}$ 23) $\frac{1}{15}$ 25) $\frac{3}{44}$

22) $\frac{4}{55}$ 24) $\frac{8}{45}$ 26) $\frac{1}{21}$

Adding Mixed Numbers

1) $5\frac{19}{45}$ 8) $5\frac{5}{63}$ 15) $5\frac{5}{7}$ 22) $5\frac{29}{30}$

2) $6\frac{19}{35}$ 9) $3\frac{29}{36}$ 16) $5\frac{2}{3}$ 23) $5\frac{5}{42}$

3) $6\frac{3}{35}$ 10) $6\frac{11}{18}$ 17) $5\frac{16}{25}$ 24) $6\frac{5}{24}$

4) $5\frac{6}{35}$ 11) $4\frac{1}{2}$ 18) $5\frac{4}{15}$ 25) $4\frac{19}{34}$

5) $3\frac{7}{30}$ 12) $5\frac{1}{10}$ 19) $8\frac{4}{21}$ 26) $2\frac{1}{2}$

6) $4\frac{59}{63}$ 13) $5\frac{5}{12}$ 20) $5\frac{7}{8}$

7) $5\frac{23}{24}$ 14) $6\frac{13}{22}$ 21) $4\frac{17}{21}$

Subtracting Mixed Numbers

1) $2\frac{8}{45}$ 8) $2\frac{22}{63}$ 15) $2\frac{8}{15}$ 22) $1\frac{13}{35}$

2) $4\frac{16}{35}$ 9) $1\frac{5}{24}$ 16) $1\frac{13}{34}$ 23) $1\frac{1}{24}$

3) $2\frac{4}{35}$ 10) $2\frac{11}{36}$ 17) $3\frac{11}{21}$ 24) $2\frac{11}{36}$

4) $6\frac{5}{8}$ 11) $4\frac{11}{18}$ 18) $1\frac{1}{3}$ 25) $2\frac{8}{25}$

5) $2\frac{11}{21}$ 12) $1\frac{13}{24}$ 19) $2\frac{1}{6}$ 26) $6\frac{5}{24}$

6) $1\frac{3}{4}$ 13) $1\frac{1}{8}$ 20) $2\frac{11}{18}$

7) $1\frac{31}{72}$ 14) $2\frac{5}{16}$ 21) $4\frac{13}{63}$

Multiplying Mixed Numbers

1) $1\frac{31}{32}$ 6) $23\frac{1}{3}$ 11) $23\frac{3}{4}$ 16) $14\frac{22}{35}$

2) $7\frac{11}{35}$ 7) $20\frac{7}{12}$ 12) $14\frac{13}{27}$ 17) $18\frac{5}{24}$

3) $2\frac{43}{72}$ 8) $22\frac{23}{40}$ 13) $18\frac{5}{12}$ 18) $16\frac{1}{4}$

4) $5\frac{7}{10}$ 9) $17\frac{11}{15}$ 14) $36\frac{2}{5}$ 19) $30\frac{2}{5}$

5) $8\frac{1}{2}$ 10) $12\frac{4}{21}$ 15) $17\frac{17}{24}$ 20) $11\frac{3}{8}$

21) $21\frac{8}{15}$ 23) $21\frac{7}{12}$ 25) $14\frac{9}{20}$

22) $13\frac{1}{7}$ 24) $25\frac{13}{35}$ 26) $26\frac{1}{15}$

Dividing Mixed Numbers

1) $3\frac{17}{26}$

2) $1\frac{39}{56}$

3) $2\frac{33}{64}$

4) $1\frac{49}{51}$

5) $1\frac{73}{75}$

6) $\frac{42}{55}$

7) $1\frac{77}{95}$

8) $3\frac{3}{80}$

9) $2\frac{53}{140}$

10) $\frac{2}{3}$

11) $2\frac{88}{105}$

12) $\frac{95}{98}$

13) $1\frac{12}{31}$

14) $1\frac{53}{136}$

15) $2\frac{10}{77}$

16) $\frac{64}{95}$

17) $1\frac{47}{68}$

18) $\frac{55}{64}$

19) $2\frac{13}{21}$

20) $1\frac{19}{32}$

21) $1\frac{31}{84}$

22) $1\frac{3}{14}$

23) $2\frac{7}{24}$

24) $1\frac{19}{56}$

25) $\frac{84}{115}$

26) $\frac{51}{77}$

Chapter 2:

Decimals

Math Topics that you'll learn in this Chapter:

- ✓ Comparing Decimals
- ✓ Rounding Decimals
- ✓ Adding and Subtracting Decimals
- ✓ Multiplying and Dividing Decimals

Comparing Decimals

✎ *Compare. Use >, =, and <*

1) 0.88 ☐ 0.088

2) 0.56 ☐ 0.57

3) 0.99 ☐ 0.89

4) 1.55 ☐ 1.65

5) 1.58 ☐ 1.75

6) 2.91 ☐ 2.85

7) 14.56 ☐ 1.456

8) 17.85 ☐ 17.89

9) 21.52 ☐ 21.052

10) 11.12 ☐ 11.03

11) 9.650 ☐ 9.65

12) 8.578 ☐ 8.568

13) 3.15 ☐ 0.315

14) 16.61 ☐ 16.16

15) 18.581 ☐ 8.991

16) 25.05 ☐ 2.505

17) 4.55 ☐ 4.65

18) 0.158 ☐ 1.58

19) 0.881 ☐ 0.871

20) 0.505 ☐ 0.510

21) 0.772 ☐ 0.777

22) 0.5 ☐ 0.500

23) 16.89 ☐ 15.89

24) 12.25 ☐ 12.35

25) 5.82 ☐ 5.69

26) 1.320 ☐ 1.032

27) 0.082 ☐ 0.088

28) 0.99 ☐ 0.099

29) 2.560 ☐ 1.950

30) 0.770 ☐ 0.707

31) 15.54 ☐ 1.554

32) 0.323 ☐ 0.332

Rounding Decimals

✎ *Round each number to the underlined place value.*

1) 2.814 =

2) 3.562 =

3) 12.125 =

4) 15.5 =

5) 1.981 =

6) 14.215 =

7) 17.548 =

8) 25.508 =

9) 31.089 =

10) 69.345 =

11) 9.457 =

12) 12.901 =

13) 2.658 =

14) 32.565 =

15) 6.058 =

16) 98.108 =

17) 27.705 =

18) 36.75 =

19) 9.08 =

20) 7.185 =

21) 22.547 =

22) 66.098 =

23) 87.75 =

24) 18.541 =

25) 10.258 =

26) 13.456 =

27) 71.084 =

28) 29.23 =

29) 45.55 =

30) 91.08 =

31) 83.433 =

32) 74.64 =

Adding and Subtracting Decimals

✎ *Solve.*

1) $15.63 + 19.64 =$

2) $16.38 + 17.59 =$

3) $75.31 - 59.69 =$

4) $49.38 - 29.89 =$

5) $24.32 + 26.45 =$

6) $36.25 + 18.37 =$

7) $47.85 - 35.12 =$

8) $85.65 - 67.48 =$

9) $25.49 + 34.18 =$

10) $19.99 + 48.66 =$

11) $46.32 - 27.77 =$

12) $54.62 - 48.12 =$

13) $24.42 + 16.54 =$

14) $52.13 + 12.32 =$

15) $82.36 - 78.65 =$

16) $64.12 - 49.15 =$

17) $36.41 + 24.52 =$

18) $85.96 - 74.63 =$

19) $52.62 - 42.54 =$

20) $21.20 + 24.58 =$

21) $32.15 + 17.17 =$

22) $96.32 - 85.54 =$

23) $89.78 - 69.85 =$

24) $29.28 + 39.79 =$

25) $11.11 + 19.99 =$

26) $28.82 + 20.88 =$

27) $63.14 - 28.91 =$

28) $56.61 - 49.72 =$

29) $26.13 + 31.13 =$

30) $30.19 + 20.87 =$

31) $66.24 - 59.10 =$

32) $89.31 - 72.17 =$

Multiplying and Dividing Decimals

✎ *Solve.*

1) $11.2 \times 0.4 =$

2) $13.5 \times 0.8 =$

3) $42.2 \div 2 =$

4) $54.6 \div 6 =$

5) $23.1 \times 0.3 =$

6) $1.2 \times 0.7 =$

7) $5.5 \div 0.5 =$

8) $64.8 \div 8 =$

9) $1.4 \times 0.5 =$

10) $4.5 \times 0.3 =$

11) $88.8 \div 4 =$

12) $10.5 \div 5 =$

13) $2.2 \times 0.3 =$

14) $0.2 \times 0.52 =$

15) $95.7 \div 100 =$

16) $36.6 \div 6 =$

17) $3.2 \times 2 =$

18) $4.1 \times 0.5 =$

19) $68.4 \div 2 =$

20) $27.9 \div 9 =$

21) $3.5 \times 4 =$

22) $4.8 \times 0.5 =$

23) $6.4 \div 4 =$

24) $72.8 \div 0.8 =$

25) $1.8 \times 3 =$

26) $6.5 \times 0.2 =$

27) $93.6 \div 3 =$

28) $45.15 \div 0.5 =$

29) $13.2 \times 0.4 =$

30) $11.2 \times 5 =$

31) $7.2 \div 0.8 =$

32) $96.4 \div 0.2 =$

Answers – Chapter 2

Comparing Decimals

1) $0.88 > 0.088$
2) $0.56 < 0.57$
3) $0.99 > 0.89$
4) $1.55 < 1.65$
5) $1.58 < 1.75$
6) $2.91 > 2.85$
7) $14.56 > 1.456$
8) $17.85 < 17.89$
9) $21.52 > 21.052$
10) $11.12 > 11.03$
11) $9.650 = 9.65$

12) $8.578 > 8.568$
13) $3.15 > 0.315$
14) $16.61 > 16.16$
15) $18.581 > 8.991$
16) $25.05 > 2.505$
17) $4.55 < 4.65$
18) $0.158 < 1.58$
19) $0.881 > 0.871$
20) $0.505 < 0.510$
21) $0.772 < 0.777$
22) $0.5 = 0.500$

23) $16.89 > 15.89$
24) $12.25 < 12.35$
25) $5.82 > 5.69$
26) $1.320 > 1.032$
27) $0.082 < 0.088$
28) $0.99 > 0.099$
29) $2.560 > 1.950$
30) $0.770 > 0.707$
31) $15.54 > 1.554$
32) $0.323 < 0.332$

Rounding Decimals

1) $\underline{2}.814 = 3$
2) $3.5\underline{6}2 = 3.56$
3) $12.1\underline{2}5 = 12.13$
4) $1\underline{5}.5 = 16$
5) $1.9\underline{8}1 = 1.98$
6) $14.\underline{2}15 = 14.2$
7) $17.5\underline{4}8 = 17.55$
8) $25.5\underline{0}8 = 25.51$
9) $3\underline{1}.089 = 31$
10) $69.\underline{3}45 = 69.3$
11) $9.4\underline{5}7 = 9.46$

12) $1\underline{2}.901 = 13$
13) $2.6\underline{5}8 = 2.66$
14) $32.\underline{5}65 = 32.6$
15) $6.0\underline{5}8 = 6.06$
16) $98.1\underline{0}8 = 98.11$
17) $27.\underline{7}05 = 27.7$
18) $3\underline{6}.75 = 37$
19) $9.\underline{0}8 = 9.1$
20) $7.\underline{1}85 = 7.2$
21) $22.5\underline{4}7 = 22.55$
22) $66.\underline{0}98 = 66.1$

23) $8\underline{7}.75 = 88$
24) $18.\underline{5}41 = 18.5$
25) $10.2\underline{5}8 = 10.26$
26) $13.\underline{4}56 = 13.5$
27) $71.0\underline{8}4 = 71.08$
28) $2\underline{9}.23 = 29$
29) $45.\underline{5}5 = 45.6$
30) $9\underline{1}.08 = 91$
33) $8\underline{3}.433 = 83$
34) $74.\underline{6}4 = 74.6$

Adding and Subtracting Decimals

1) 35.27
2) 33.97
3) 15.62
4) 19.49
5) 50.77
6) 54.62
7) 12.73
8) 18.17
9) 59.67
10) 68.65

11) 18.55
12) 6.5
13) 40.96
14) 64.45
15) 3.71
16) 14.97
17) 60.93
18) 11.33
19) 10.08
20) 45.78

21) 49.32
22) 10.78
23) 19.93
24) 69.07
25) 31.1
26) 49.7
27) 34.23
28) 6.89
29) 57.26
30) 51.06

31) 7.14   32) 17.14

Multiplying and Dividing Decimals

1) 4.48
2) 10.8
3) 21.1
4) 9.1
5) 6.93
6) 0.84
7) 1.1
8) 8.1
9) 0.7
10) 1.35
11) 22.2

12) 2.1
13) 0.66
14) 0.104
15) 0.957
16) 6.1
17) 6.4
18) 2.05
19) 34.2
20) 3.1
21) 14
22) 2.4

23) 1.6
24) 91
25) 5.4
26) 1.3
27) 31.2
28) 90.3
29) 5.28
30) 56
31) 9
32) 482

Chapter 3:

Integers and Order of Operations

Math Topics that you'll learn in this Chapter:

- ✓ Adding and Subtracting Integers

- ✓ Multiplying and Dividing Integers

- ✓ Order of Operations

- ✓ Integers and Absolute Value

Adding and Subtracting Integers

✎ *Solve.*

1) $-(8) + 13 =$

2) $17 - (-12 - 8) =$

3) $(-15) + (-4) =$

4) $(-14) + (-8) + 9 =$

5) $-(23) + 19 =$

6) $(-7 + 5) - 9 =$

7) $28 + (-32) =$

8) $(-11) + (-9) + 5 =$

9) $25 - (8 - 7) =$

10) $-(29) + 17 =$

11) $(-38) + (-3) + 29 =$

12) $15 - (-7 + 9) =$

13) $24 - (8 - 2) =$

14) $(-7 + 4) - 9 =$

15) $(-17) + (-3) + 9 =$

16) $(-26) + (-7) + 8 =$

17) $(-9) + (-11) =$

18) $8 - (-23 - 13) =$

19) $(-16) + (-2) =$

20) $25 - (7 - 4) =$

21) $23 + (-12) =$

22) $(-18) + (-6) =$

23) $17 - (-21 - 7) =$

24) $-(28) - (-16) + 5 =$

25) $(-9 + 4) - 8 =$

26) $(-28) + (-6) + 17 =$

27) $-(21) - (-15) + 9 =$

28) $(-31) + (-6) =$

29) $(-17) + (-11) + 14 =$

30) $(-29) + (-10) + 13 =$

31) $-(24) - (-12) + 5 =$

32) $8 - (-19 - 10) =$

Multiplying and Dividing Integers

✎ *Solve.*

1) $(-9) \times (-8) =$

2) $6 \times (-6) =$

3) $49 \div (-7) =$

4) $(-64) \div 8 =$

5) $(4) \times (-6) =$

6) $(-9) \times (-11) =$

7) $(10) \div (-5) =$

8) $144 \div (-12) =$

9) $(10) \times (-2) =$

10) $(-8) \times (-2) \times 5 =$

11) $(8) \div (-2) =$

12) $45 \div (-15) =$

13) $(5) \times (-7) =$

14) $(-6) \times (-5) \times 4 =$

15) $(12) \div (-6) =$

16) $(14) \div (-7) =$

17) $196 \div (-14) =$

18) $(27 - 13) \times (-2) =$

19) $125 \div (-5) =$

20) $66 \div (-6) =$

21) $(-6) \times (-5) \times 3 =$

22) $(15 - 6) \times (-3) =$

23) $(32 - 24) \div (-4) =$

24) $72 \div (-6) =$

25) $(-14 + 8) \times (-7) =$

26) $(-3) \times (-9) \times 3 =$

27) $84 \div (-12) =$

28) $(-12) \times (-10) =$

29) $25 \times (-4) =$

30) $(-3) \times (-5) \times 5 =$

31) $(15) \div (-3) =$

32) $(-18) \div (3) =$

Order of Operation

✎ *Calculate.*

1) $18 + (32 \div 4) =$

2) $(3 \times 8) \div (-2) =$

3) $67 - (4 \times 8) =$

4) $(-11) \times (8 - 3) =$

5) $(18 - 7) \times (6) =$

6) $(6 \times 10) \div (12 + 3) =$

7) $(13 \times 2) - (24 \div 6) =$

8) $(-5) + (4 \times 3) + 8 =$

9) $(4 \times 2^3) + (16 - 9) =$

10) $(3^2 \times 7) \div (-2 + 1) =$

11) $[-2(48 \div 2^3)] - 6 =$

12) $(-4) + (7 \times 8) + 18 =$

13) $(3 \times 7) + (16 - 7) =$

14) $[3^3 \times (48 \div 2^3)] \div (-2) =$

15) $(14 \times 3) - (3^4 \div 9) =$

16) $(96 \div 12) \times (-3) =$

17) $(48 \div 2^2) \times (-2) =$

18) $(56 \div 7) \times (-5) =$

19) $(-2^2) + (7 \times 9) - 21 =$

20) $(2^4 - 9) \times (-6) =$

21) $[4^3 \times (50 \div 5^2)] \div (-16) =$

22) $(3^2 \times 4^2) \div (-4 + 2) =$

23) $6^2 - (-6 \times 4) + 3 =$

24) $4^2 - (5^2 \times 3) =$

25) $(-4) + (12^2 \div 3^2) - 7^2 =$

26) $(3^2 \times 5) + (-5^2 - 9) =$

27) $2[(3^2 \times 5) \times (-6)] =$

28) $(11^2 - 2^2) - (-7^2) =$

29) $(2^3 \times 3) - (49 \div 7) =$

30) $3[(3^2 \times 5) + (25 \div 5)] =$

31) $(6^2 \times 5) \div (-5) =$

32) $2^2[(6^3 \div 12) - (3^4 \div 27)] =$

Integers and Absolute Value

✎ *Calculate.*

1) $5 - |8 - 12| =$

2) $|15| - \frac{|-1|}{4} =$

3) $\frac{|9 \times -6|}{18} \times \frac{|-24|}{8} =$

4) $|13 \times 3| + \frac{|-7|}{9} =$

5) $4 - |11 - 18| - |3| =$

6) $|18| - \frac{|-12|}{4} =$

7) $\frac{|5 \times -8|}{10} \times \frac{|-22|}{11} =$

8) $|9 \times 3| + \frac{|-3|}{4} =$

9) $|-42 + 7| \times \frac{|-2 \times 5|}{10} =$

10) $6 - |17 - 11| - |5| =$

11) $|13| - \frac{|-54|}{6} =$

12) $\frac{|9 \times -4|}{12} \times \frac{|-4|}{9} =$

13) $|-75 + 50| \times \frac{|-4 \times 5|}{5} =$

14) $\frac{|-26|}{13} \times \frac{|-32|}{8} =$

15) $14 - |8 - 18| - |-12| =$

16) $|29| - \frac{|-2|}{5} =$

17) $\frac{|3 \times 8|}{2} \times \frac{|-33|}{3} =$

18) $|-45 + 15| \times \frac{|-1 \times 5|}{6} =$

19) $\frac{|-50|}{5} \times \frac{|-77|}{11} =$

20) $12 - |2 - 7| - |15| =$

21) $|18| - \frac{|-45|}{15} =$

22) $\frac{|7 \times 8|}{4} \times \frac{|-48|}{12} =$

23) $\frac{|30 \times 2|}{3} \times |-12| =$

24) $\frac{|-36|}{9} \times \frac{|-80|}{8} =$

25) $|-35 + 8| \times \frac{|-9 \times 5|}{15} =$

26) $|19| - \frac{|-18|}{2} =$

27) $14 - |11 - 23| + |2| =$

28) $|-39 + 7| \times \frac{|-4 \times 6|}{3} =$

Answers – Chapter 3

Adding and Subtracting Integers

1) 5
2) 37
3) −19
4) −13
5) −4
6) −11
7) −4
8) −15
9) 24
10) −12
11) −12

12) 13
13) 18
14) −12
15) −11
16) −25
17) −20
18) 44
19) −18
20) 22
21) 11
22) −24

23) 45
24) −7
25) −13
26) −17
27) 3
28) −37
29) −14
30) −26
31) −7
32) 37

Multiplying and Dividing Integers

1) 72
2) −36
3) −7
4) −8
5) −24
6) 99
7) −2
8) −12
9) −20
10) 80
11) −4

12) −3
13) −35
14) 150
15) −2
16) −2
17) −14
18) −28
19) 25
20) −11
21) 90
22) −27

23) −2
24) −12
25) 42
26) 81
27) −7
28) 120
29) −100
30) 75
31) −5
32) −6

Order of Operation

1) 26
2) −12
3) 35
4) −55
5) 66
6) 4
7) 22
8) 15
9) 39
10) −63

11) −18
12) 70
13) 30
14) −81
15) 33
16) −24
17) −24
18) −40
19) 38
20) −42

21) −8
22) −72
23) 63
24) −59
25) −37
26) 11
27) −540
28) 166
29) 17
30) 150

31) −36

32) 60

Integers and Absolute Value

1) 1

2) 11

3) 9

4) 47

5) −6

6) 15

7) 8

8) 36

9) 35

10) −5

11) 4

12) 15

13) 100

14) 8

15) −8

16) 25

17) 132

18) 300

19) 70

20) −8

21) 15

22) 56

23) 240

24) 40

25) 81

26) 10

27) 4

28) 256

Chapter 4:

Ratios and Proportions

Math Topics that you'll learn in this Chapter:

- ✓ Simplifying Ratios
- ✓ Proportional Ratios
- ✓ Similarity and Ratios

Simplifying Ratios

✎ *Simplify each ratio.*

1) $3 : 27 =$ ___ : ___

2) $2 : 8 =$ ___ : ___

3) $\frac{4}{28} = -$

4) $\frac{16}{40} = -$

5) $10 : 30 =$ ___ : ___

6) $5 : 30 =$ ___ : ___

7) $\frac{34}{38} = -$

8) $\frac{45}{63} = -$

9) $10 : 45 =$ ___ : ___

10) $20 : 30 =$ ___ : ___

11) $\frac{40}{64} = -$

12) $\frac{10}{110} = -$

13) $8 : 12 =$ ___ : ___

14) $16 : 20 =$ ___ : ___

15) $\frac{24}{48} = -$

16) $\frac{21}{77} = -$

17) $8 : 24 =$ ___ : ___

18) 9 to $36 =$ ___ : ___

19) $\frac{64}{72} = -$

20) $\frac{45}{60} = -$

21) $12 : 15 =$ ___ : ___

22) $18 : 54 =$ ___ : ___

23) $\frac{36}{54} = -$

24) $\frac{48}{104} = -$

25) $15 : 75 =$ ___ : ___

26) $16 : 48 =$ ___ : ___

27) $\frac{15}{65} = -$

28) $\frac{44}{52} = -$

Proportional Ratios

✍ *Solve each proportion for x.*

1) $\frac{4}{7} = \frac{16}{x}$, $x =$ ____

2) $\frac{4}{9} = \frac{x}{18}$, $x =$ ____

3) $\frac{3}{5} = \frac{24}{x}$, $x =$ ____

4) $\frac{3}{10} = \frac{x}{50}$, $x =$ ____

5) $\frac{3}{11} = \frac{15}{x}$, $x =$ ____

6) $\frac{6}{15} = \frac{x}{45}$, $x =$ ____

7) $\frac{6}{19} = \frac{12}{x}$, $x =$ ____

8) $\frac{7}{16} = \frac{x}{32}$, $x =$ ____

9) $\frac{18}{21} = \frac{54}{x}$, $x =$ ____

10) $\frac{13}{15} = \frac{39}{x}$, $x =$ ____

11) $\frac{9}{13} = \frac{72}{x}$, $x =$ ____

12) $\frac{8}{30} = \frac{x}{180}$, $x =$ ____

13) $\frac{3}{19} = \frac{9}{x}$, $x =$ ____

14) $\frac{1}{3} = \frac{x}{90}$, $x =$ ____

15) $\frac{25}{45} = \frac{x}{9}$, $x =$ ____

16) $\frac{1}{6} = \frac{9}{x}$, $x =$ ____

17) $\frac{7}{9} = \frac{63}{x}$, $x =$ ____

18) $\frac{54}{72} = \frac{x}{8}$, $x =$ ____

19) $\frac{32}{40} = \frac{4}{x}$, $x =$ ____

20) $\frac{21}{42} = \frac{x}{6}$, $x =$ ____

21) $\frac{56}{72} = \frac{7}{x}$, $x =$ ____

22) $\frac{1}{14} = \frac{x}{42}$, $x =$ ____

23) $\frac{5}{7} = \frac{75}{x}$, $x =$ ____

24) $\frac{30}{48} = \frac{x}{8}$, $x =$ ____

25) $\frac{36}{88} = \frac{9}{x}$, $x =$ ____

26) $\frac{62}{68} = \frac{x}{34}$, $x =$ ____

27) $\frac{42}{60} = \frac{x}{10}$, $x =$ ____

28) $\frac{8}{9} = \frac{x}{108}$, $x =$ ____

29) $\frac{46}{69} = \frac{x}{3}$, $x =$ ____

30) $\frac{99}{121} = \frac{x}{11}$, $x =$ ____

31) $\frac{19}{21} = \frac{x}{63}$, $x =$ ____

32) $\frac{11}{12} = \frac{x}{48}$, $x =$ ____

Create Proportion

✍ *State if each pair of ratios form a proportion.*

1) $\frac{5}{8}$ *and* $\frac{25}{50}$

2) $\frac{2}{11}$ *and* $\frac{4}{22}$

3) $\frac{2}{5}$ *and* $\frac{8}{20}$

4) $\frac{3}{11}$ *and* $\frac{9}{33}$

5) $\frac{5}{10}$ *and* $\frac{15}{30}$

6) $\frac{4}{13}$ *and* $\frac{8}{24}$

7) $\frac{6}{9}$ *and* $\frac{24}{36}$

8) $\frac{7}{12}$ *and* $\frac{14}{20}$

9) $\frac{3}{8}$ *and* $\frac{27}{72}$

10) $\frac{12}{20}$ *and* $\frac{36}{60}$

11) $\frac{11}{12}$ *and* $\frac{55}{60}$

12) $\frac{12}{15}$ *and* $\frac{24}{25}$

13) $\frac{15}{19}$ *and* $\frac{20}{38}$

14) $\frac{10}{14}$ *and* $\frac{40}{56}$

15) $\frac{11}{13}$ *and* $\frac{44}{39}$

16) $\frac{15}{16}$ *and* $\frac{30}{32}$

17) $\frac{17}{19}$ *and* $\frac{34}{48}$

18) $\frac{5}{18}$ *and* $\frac{15}{54}$

19) $\frac{3}{14}$ *and* $\frac{18}{42}$

20) $\frac{7}{11}$ *and* $\frac{14}{32}$

21) $\frac{8}{11}$ *and* $\frac{32}{44}$

22) $\frac{9}{13}$ *and* $\frac{18}{26}$

✍ *Solve.*

23) The ratio of boys to girls in a class is 5:6. If there are 25 boys in the class, how many girls are in that class? _____

24) The ratio of red marbles to blue marbles in a bag is 4:7. If there are 77 marbles in the bag, how many of the marbles are red? _____

25) You can buy 8 cans of green beans at a supermarket for $3.20. How much does it cost to buy 48 cans of green beans? _____

Similarity and Ratios

✎ *Each pair of figures is similar. Find the missing side.*

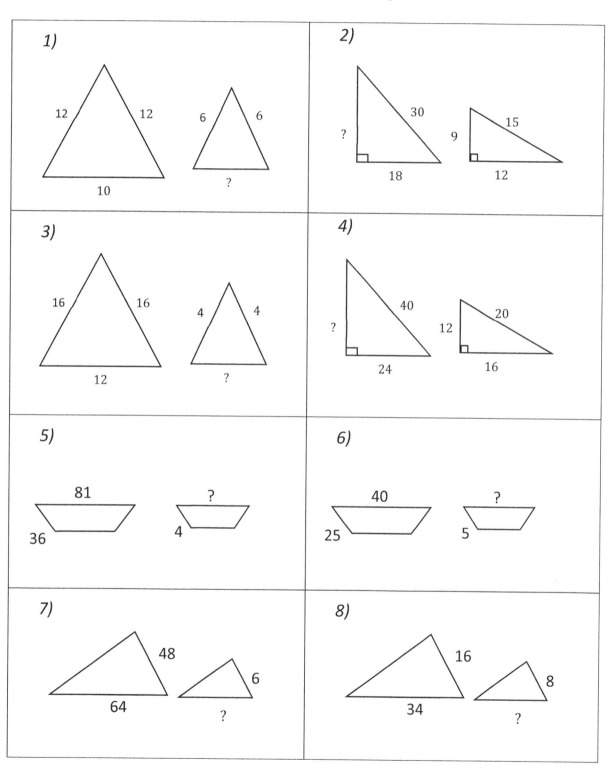

1)

12   12   6   6

10   ?

2)

30   15

?   9

18   12

3)

16   16   4   4

12   ?

4)

40   20

?   12

24   16

5)

81   ?

36   4

6)

40   ?

25   5

7)

48   6

64   ?

8)

16   8

34   ?

Answers – Chapter 4

Simplifying Ratios

1) $1:9$

2) $1:4$

3) $\frac{1}{7}$

4) $\frac{2}{5}$

5) $1:3$

6) $1:6$

7) $\frac{17}{19}$

8) $\frac{5}{7}$

9) $2:9$

10) $2:3$

11) $\frac{5}{8}$

12) $\frac{1}{11}$

13) $2:3$

14) $4:5$

15) $\frac{1}{2}$

16) $\frac{3}{11}$

17) $1:6$

18) 1 to 4

19) $\frac{8}{9}$

20) $\frac{3}{4}$

21) $4:5$

22) $1:3$

23) $\frac{2}{3}$

24) $\frac{6}{13}$

25) $1:5$

26) $1:3$

27) $\frac{3}{13}$

28) $\frac{11}{13}$

Proportional Ratios

1) $x = 28$

2) $x = 8$

3) $x = 40$

4) $x = 15$

5) $x = 55$

6) $x = 18$

7) $x = 38$

8) $x = 14$

9) $x = 63$

10) $x = 45$

11) $x = 104$

12) $x = 48$

13) $x = 57$

14) $x = 30$

15) $x = 5$

16) $x = 54$

17) $x = 81$

18) $x = 6$

19) $x = 5$

20) $x = 3$

21) $x = 9$

22) $x = 3$

23) $x = 105$

24) $x = 5$

25) $x = 22$

26) $x = 31$

27) $x = 7$

28) $x = 96$

29) $x = 2$

30) $x = 9$

31) $x = 57$

32) $x = 44$

Create Proportion

1) *No*

2) *Yes*

3) *Yes*

4) *Yes*

5) *Yes*

6) *No*

7) *Yes*

8) *No*

9) *Yes*

10) *Yes*

11) *Yes*

12) *No*

13) *No*

14) *Yes*

15) *No*

16) *Yes*

17) *Yes*

18) *Yes*

19) *No*

20) *No*

21) *Yes*

22) *Yes*

23) 30 *girls*
24) 28 *red marbles*
25) $19.20

Similarity and Ratios

1) 5
2) 24
3) 3
4) 32

5) 9
6) 8
7) 8
8) 17

Chapter 5:

Percentage

Math Topics that you'll learn in this Chapter:

- ✓ Percent Problems
- ✓ Percent of Increase and Decrease
- ✓ Simple Interest
- ✓ Discount, Tax and Tip

Percent Problems

✐ *Solve each problem.*

1) What is 5 percent of 300? ____

2) What is 15 percent of 600? ____

3) What is 12 percent of 450? ____

4) What is 30 percent of 240? ____

5) What is 60 percent of 850? ____

6) 63 is what percent of 300? ____%

7) 80 is what percent of 400? ____%

8) 70 is what percent of 700? ____%

9) 84 is what percent of 600? ___%

10) 90 is what percent of 300? ___%

11) 24 is what percent of 150? ___%

12) 12 is what percent of 80? ____%

13) 4 is what percent of 50? ____%

14) 110 is what percent of 500? _%

15) 16 is what percent of 400? __%

16) 39 is what percent of 300? ___%

17) 56 is what percent of 200? ___%

18) 30 is what percent of 500? ___%

19) 84 is what percent of 700? ___%

20) 40 is what percent of 500? __%

21) 26 is what percent of 100? __ %

22) 45 is what percent of 900? __%

23) 60 is what percent of 400? ____%

24) 18 is what percent of 900? ____%

25) 75 is what percent of 250? ____%

26) 27 is what percent of 900? ____%

27) 49 is what percent of 700? ____%

28) 81 is what percent of 900? ____%

29) 90 is what percent of 500? ____%

30) 82 is 20 percent of what number? ____

31) 14 is 35 percent of what number? ____

32) 90 is 6 percent of what number? ____

33) 80 is 40 percent of what number? ____

34) 90 is 15 percent of what number? ____

35) 28 is 7 percent of what number? ____

36) 54 is 18 percent of what number? ____

37) 72 is 24 percent of what number? ____

Percent of Increase and Decrease

✎ *Solve each percent of change word problem.*

1) Bob got a raise, and his hourly wage increased from $24 to $36. What is the percent increase? _____ %

2) The price of gasoline rose from $2.20 to $2.42 in one month. By what percent did the gas price rise? _____ %

3) In a class, the number of students has been increased from 30 to 39. What is the percent increase? _____ %

4) The price of a pair of shoes increases from $28 to $35. What is the percent increase? ___ %

5) In a class, the number of students has been decreased from 24 to 18. What is the percentage decrease? _____ %

6) Nick got a raise, and his hourly wage increased from $50 to $55. What is the percent increase? _____ %

7) A coat was originally priced at $80. It went on sale for $70.40. What was the percent that the coat was discounted? _____ %

8) The price of a pair of shoes increases from $8 to $12. What is the percent increase? ___ %

9) A house was purchased in 2002 for $180,000. It is now valued at $144,000. What is the rate (percent) of depreciation for the house?_____ %

10) The price of gasoline rose from $3.00 to $3.15 in one month. By what percent did the gas price rise? _____ %

Simple Interest

✎ *Determine the simple interest for these loans.*

1) $440 at 5% for 6 years. $___

2) $460 at 2.5% for 4 years. $_

3) $500 at 3% for 5 years. $___

4) $550 at 9% for 2 years. $___

5) $690 at 5% for 6 months. $___

6) $620 at 7% for 3 years. $___

7) $650 at 4.5% for 10 years. $___

8) $850 at 4% for 2 years. $___

9) $640 at 7% for 3 years. $___

10) $300 at 9% for 9 months. $___

11) $760 at 8% for 2 years. $_

12) $910 at 5% for 5 years. $___

13) $540 at 3% for 6 years. $___

14) $780 at 2.5% for 4 years. $___

15) $1,600 at 7% for 3 months. $___

16) $310 at 4% for 4 years. $___

17) $950 at 6% for 5 years. $___

18) $280 at 8% for 7 years. $___

19) $310 at 6% for 3 years. $___

20) $990 at 5% for 4 months. $___

21) $380 at 6% for 5 years. $___

22) $580 at 6% for 4 years. $___

23) $1,200 at 4% for5 years. $___

24) $3,100 at 5% for 6 years. $___

25) $5,200 at 8% for 2 years. $___

26) $1,400 at 4% for 3 years. $___

27) $300 at 3% for 8 months. $___

28) $150 at 3.5% for 4 years. $___

29) $170 at 6% for 2 years. $___

30) $940 at 8% for 5 years. $___

31) $960 at 1.5% for 8 years. $_

32) $240 at 5% for 4 months. $___

33) $280 at 2% for 5 years. $___

34) $880 at 3% for 2 years. $___

35) $2,200 at 4.5% for 2 years. $___

36) $2,400 at 7% for 3 years. $___

37) $1,800 at 5% for 6 months. $___

38) $190 at 4% for 2 years. $___

39) $560 at 7% for 4 years. $___

40) $720 at 8% for 2 years. $_

41) $780 at 5% for 8 years. $___

42) $880 at 6% for 3 months. $___

Discount, Tax and Tip

✍ *Find the missing values.*

1) Original price of a computer: $400

   Tax: 5%, Selling price: $_____

2) Original price of a sofa: $600

   Tax: 12%, Selling price: $_____

3) Original price of a table: $550

   Tax: 18%, Selling price: $_____

4) Original price of a cell phone: $700

   Tax: 20%, Selling price: $_____

5) Original price of a printer: $400

   Tax: 22%, Selling price: $_____

6) Original price of a computer: $600

   Tax: 15%, Selling price: $_____

7) Restaurant bill: $24.00

   Tip: 25%, Final amount: $_____

8) Original price of a cell phone: $300

   Tax: 8%, Selling price: $_____

9) Original price of a carpet: $800

   Tax: 25%, Selling price: $_____

10) Original price of a camera: $200

    Discount: 35%, Selling price: $_____

11) Original price of a dress: $500

    Discount: 10%, Selling price: $_____

12) Original price of a monitor: $400

    Discount: 5%, Selling price: $_____

13) Original price of a laptop: $900

    Discount: 20%, Selling price: $_____

14) Restaurant bill: $54.00

    Tip: 20%, Final amount: $_____

Answers – Chapter 5

Percent Problems

1) 15
2) 90
3) 54
4) 72
5) 510
6) 21%
7) 20%
8) 10%
9) 14%
10) 30%
11) 16%
12) 15%
13) 8%

14) 22%
15) 4%
16) 13%
17) 28%
18) 6%
19) 12%
20) 8%
21) 26%
22) 5%
23) 15%
24) 2%
25) 30%
26) 3%

27) 7%
28) 9%
29) 18%
30) 410
31) 40
32) 1,500
33) 200
34) 600
35) 400
36) 300
37) 300

Percent of Increase and Decrease - Answers

1) 50%
2) 10%
3) 30%
4) 25%

5) 25%
6) 10%
7) 12%
8) 50%

9) 20%
10) 5%

Simple Interest

2) $132
3) $46
4) $75
5) $99
6) $17.25
7) $130.20
8) $292.50
9) $68
10) $134.40
11) $20.25
12) $121.60
13) $227.50
14) $97.20
15) $78

16) $28
17) $49.60
18) $285
19) $156.80
20) $55.80
21) $198
22) $114
23) $139.20
24) $240
25) $930
26) $832
27) $168
28) $6
29) $21

30) $20.40
31) $376
32) $115.20
33) $4
34) $28
35) $52.80
36) $198
37) $504
38) $45
39) $15.20
40) $156.80
41) $115.20
42) $312
43) $13.20

Discount, Tax and Tip - Answers

1) $420
2) $672
3) $649
4) $840
5) $488
6) $690
7) $30.00

8) $324
9) $1,000
10) $130
11) $450
12) $380
13) $720
14) $64.80

Chapter 6:

Expressions and Variables

Math Topics that you'll learn in this Chapter:

✓ Simplifying Variable Expressions

✓ Simplifying Polynomial Expressions

✓ Evaluating One Variable

✓ Evaluating Two Variables

✓ The Distributive Property

Simplifying Variable Expressions

✎ *Simplify and write the answer.*

1) $3x + 5 + 2x =$

2) $7x + 3 - 3x =$

3) $-2 - x^2 - 6x^2 =$

4) $(-6)(8x - 4) =$

5) $3 + 10x^2 + 2x =$

6) $8x^2 + 6x + 7x^2 =$

7) $2x^2 - 5x - 7x =$

8) $x - 3 + 5 - 3x =$

9) $2 - 3x + 12 - 2x =$

10) $5x^2 - 12x^2 + 8x =$

11) $2x^2 + 6x + 3x^2 =$

12) $2x^2 - 2x - x =$

13) $2x^2 - (-8x + 6) = 2$

14) $4x + 6(2 - 5x) =$

15) $10x + 8(10x - 6) =$

16) $9(-2x - 6) - 5 =$

17) $32x - 4 + 23 + 2x =$

18) $8x - 12x - x^2 + 13 =$

19) $(-6)(8x - 4) + 10x =$

20) $14x - 5(5 - 8x) =$

21) $23x + 4(9x + 3) + 12 =$

22) $3(-7x + 5) + 20x =$

23) $12x - 3x(x + 9) =$

24) $7x + 5x(3 - 3x) =$

25) $5x(-8x + 12) + 14x =$

26) $40x + 12 + 2x^2 =$

27) $5x(x - 3) - 10 =$

28) $8x - 7 + 8x + 2x^2 =$

29) $7x - 3x^2 - 5x^2 - 3 =$

30) $4 + x^2 - 6x^2 - 12x =$

31) $12x + 8x^2 + 2x + 20 =$

32) $23 + 15x^2 + 8x - 4x^2 =$

Simplifying Polynomial Expressions

✎ *Simplify and write the answer.*

1) $(2x^3 + 5x^2) - (12x + 2x^2) =$ _____

2) $(-x^5 + 2x^3) - (3x^3 + 6x^2) =$ _____

3) $(12x^4 + 4x^2) - (2x^2 - 6x^4) =$ _____

4) $4x - 3x^2 - 2(6x^2 + 6x^3) =$ _____

5) $(2x^3 - 3) + 3(2x^2 - 3x^3) =$ _____

6) $4(4x^3 - 2x) - (3x^3 - 2x^4) =$ _____

7) $2(4x - 3x^3) - 3(3x^3 + 4x^2) =$ _____

8) $(2x^2 - 2x) - (2x^3 + 5x^2) =$ _____

9) $2x^3 - (4x^4 + 2x) + x^2 =$ _____

10) $x^4 - 9(x^2 + x) - 5x =$ _____

11) $(-2x^2 - x^4) + (4x^4 - x^2) =$ _____

12) $4x^2 - 5x^3 + 15x^4 - 12x^3 =$ _____

13) $2x^2 - 5x^4 + 14x^4 - 11x^3 =$ _____

14) $2x^2 + 5x^3 - 7x^2 + 12x =$ _____

15) $2x^4 - 5x^5 + 8x^4 - 8x^2 =$ _____

16) $5x^3 + 17x - 5x^2 - 2x^3 =$ _____

Evaluating One Variable

✑ *Evaluate each expression using the value given.*

1) $x = 3 \Rightarrow 6x - 9 =$

2) $x = 2 \Rightarrow 7x - 10 =$

3) $x = 1 \Rightarrow 5x + 2 =$

4) $x = 2 \Rightarrow 3x + 9 =$

5) $x = 4 \Rightarrow 4x - 8 =$

6) $x = 2 \Rightarrow 5x - 2x + 10 =$

7) $x = 3 \Rightarrow 2x - x - 6 =$

8) $x = 4 \Rightarrow 6x - 3x + 4 =$

9) $x = -2 \Rightarrow 4x - 6x - 5 =$

10) $x = -1 \Rightarrow 3x - 5x + 11 =$

11) $x = 1 \Rightarrow x - 7x + 12 =$

12) $x = 2 \Rightarrow 2(-3x + 4) =$

13) $x = 3 \Rightarrow 4(-5x - 2) =$

14) $x = 2 \Rightarrow 5(-2x - 4) =$

15) $x = -2 \Rightarrow 3(-4x - 5) =$

16) $x = 3 \Rightarrow 8x + 5 =$

17) $x = -3 \Rightarrow 12x + 9 =$

18) $x = -1 \Rightarrow 9x - 8 =$

19) $x = 2 \Rightarrow 16x - 10 =$

20) $x = 1 \Rightarrow 4x + 3 =$

21) $x = 5 \Rightarrow 7x - 2 =$

22) $x = 7 \Rightarrow 28 - x =$

23) $x = 3 \Rightarrow 5x - 10 =$

24) $x = 12 \Rightarrow 40 - 2x =$

25) $x = 2 \Rightarrow 11x - 2 =$

26) $x = 3 \Rightarrow 2x - x + 10 =$

Evaluating Two Variables

✎ *Evaluate each expression using the values given.*

1) $2x + 3y, x = 2, y = 3$

____

2) $3x + 4y, x = -1, y = -2$

____

3) $x + 6y, x = 3, y = 1$

____

4) $2a - (15 - b), a = 2, b = 3$

____

5) $4a - (6 - 3b), a = 1, b = 4$

____

6) $a - (8 - 2b), a = 2, b = 5$

____

7) $3z + 21 + 5k, z = 4, k = 1$

____

8) $-7a + 4b, a = 6, b = 3$

____

9) $-4a + 3b, a = 2, b = 4$

____

10) $-6a + 6b, a = 4, b = 3$

____

11) $-8a + 2b, a = 4, b = 6$

____

12) $4x + 6y, x = 6, y = 3$

____

13) $2x + 9y, x = 8, y = 1$

____

14) $x - 7y, x = 9, y = 4$

____

15) $5x - 4y, x = 6, y = 3$

____

16) $2z + 14 + 8k, z = 4, k = 1$

____

17) $6x + 3y, x = 3, y = 8$

____

18) $5a - 6b, a = -3, b = -1$

____

19) $8a + 4b, a = -4, b = 3$

____

20) $-2a - b, a = 4, b = 9$

____

21) $-7a + 3b, a = 4, b = 3$

____

22) $-5a + 9b, a = 7, b = 1$

____

The Distributive Property

✎ *Use the distributive property to simply each expression.*

1) $(-3)(12x + 3) =$

2) $(-4x + 5)(-6) =$

3) $13(-4x + 2) =$

4) $7(6 - 3x) =$

5) $(6 - 5x)(-4) =$

6) $9(8 - 2x) =$

7) $(-4x + 6)5 =$

8) $(-2x + 7)(-8) =$

9) $8(-4x + 7) =$

10) $(-9x + 5)(-3) =$

11) $8(-x + 9) =$

12) $7(2 - 6x) =$

13) $(-12x + 4)(-3) =$

14) $(-6)(-10x + 6) =$

15) $(-5)(5 - 11x) =$

16) $9(4 - 8x) =$

17) $(-6x + 2)7 =$

18) $(-9)(1 - 12x) =$

19) $(-3)(4 - 6x) =$

20) $(2 - 8x)(-2) =$

21) $20(2 - x) =$

22) $12(-4x + 3) =$

23) $15(2 - 3x) =$

24) $(-4x + 5)2 =$

25) $(-11x + 8)(-2) =$

26) $14(5 - 8x) =$

Answers – Chapter 6

Simplifying Variable Expressions

1) $5x + 5$
2) $4x + 3$
3) $-7x^2 - 2$
4) $-48x + 24$
5) $10x^2 + 2x + 3$
6) $15x^2 + 6x$
7) $2x^2 - 12x$
8) $-2x + 2$
9) $-5x + 14$
10) $-7x^2 + 8x$
11) $5x^2 + 6x$
12) $2x^2 - 3x$
13) $2x^2 + 8x - 6$
14) $-26x + 12$
15) $90x - 48$
16) $-18x - 59$
17) $34x + 19$
18) $-x^2 - 4x + 13$
19) $-38x + 24$
20) $54x - 25$
21) $59x + 24$
22) $-x + 15$
23) $-3x^2 - 15x$
24) $-15x^2 + 22x$
25) $-40x^2 + 74x$
26) $2x^2 + 40x + 12$
27) $5x^2 - 15x - 10$
28) $2x^2 + 16x - 7$
29) $-8x^2 + 7x - 3$
30) $-5x^2 - 12x + 4$
31) $8x^2 + 14x + 20$
32) $11x^2 + 8x + 23$

Simplifying Polynomial Expressions

1) $2x^3 + 3x^2 - 12x$
2) $-x^5 - x^3 - 6x^2$
3) $18x^4 + 2x^2$
4) $-12x^3 - 15x^2 + 4x$
5) $-7x^3 + 6x^2 - 3$
6) $2x^4 + 13x^3 - 8x$
7) $-15x^3 - 12x^2 + 8x$
14) $5x^3 - 5x^2 + 12x$
15) $-5x^5 + 10x^4 - 8x^2$
8) $-2x^3 - 3x^2 - 2x$
9) $-4x^4 + 2x^3 + x^2 - 2x$
10) $x^4 - 9x^2 - 14x$
11) $3x^4 - 3x^2$
12) $15x^4 - 17x^3 + 4x^2$
13) $9x^4 - 11x^3 + 2x^2$
16) $3x^3 - 5x^2 + 17x$

Evaluating One Variable

1) 9
2) 4
3) 7
4) 15
5) 8
6) 16
7) -3
8) 16
9) -1
10) 13
11) 6
12) -4
13) -68
14) -40
15) 9
16) 29
17) -27
18) -17
19) 22
20) 7
21) 33

22) 21

23) 5

24) 16

25) 20

26) 13

Evaluating Two Variables

1) 13
2) −11
3) 9
4) −8
5) 10
6) 4
7) 38
8) −30

9) 4
10) 6
11) −20
12) 42
13) 25
14) −19
15) 18
16) 30

17) 42
18) −9
19) −20
20) −17
21) −19
22) −26

The Distributive Property

1) $-36x - 9$
2) $24x - 30$
3) $-52x + 26$
4) $-21x + 42$
5) $20x - 24$
6) $-18x + 72$
7) $-20x + 30$
8) $16x - 56$
9) $-32x + 56$

10) $27x - 15$
11) $-8x + 72$
12) $-42x + 14$
13) $36x - 12$
14) $60x - 36$
15) $55x - 25$
16) $-72x + 36$
17) $-42x + 14$
18) $108x - 9$

19) $18x - 12$
20) $16x - 4$
21) $-20x + 40$
22) $-48x + 36$
23) $-45x + 30$
24) $-8x + 10$
25) $22x - 16$
26) $-112x + 70$

Chapter 7:

Equations and Inequalities

Math Topics that you'll learn in this Chapter:

- ✓ One–Step Equations

- ✓ Multi–Step Equations

- ✓ System of Equations

- ✓ Graphing Single–Variable Inequalities

- ✓ One–Step Inequalities

- ✓ Multi–Step Inequalities

One–Step Equations

✎ *Solve each equation for x.*

1) $x - 15 = 24 \Rightarrow x =$ _____

2) $18 = -6 + x \Rightarrow x =$ _____

3) $19 - x = 8 \Rightarrow x =$ _____

4) $x - 22 = 24 \Rightarrow x =$ _____

5) $24 - x = 17 \Rightarrow x =$ _____

6) $16 - x = 3 \Rightarrow x =$ _____

7) $x + 14 = 12 \Rightarrow x =$ _____

8) $26 + x = 8 \Rightarrow x =$ _____

9) $x + 9 = -18 \Rightarrow x =$ _____

10) $x + 21 = 11 \Rightarrow x =$ _____

11) $17 = -5 + x \Rightarrow x =$ _____

12) $x + 20 = 29 \Rightarrow x =$ _____

13) $x - 13 = 19 \Rightarrow x =$ _____

14) $x + 9 = -17 \Rightarrow x =$ _____

15) $x + 4 = -23 \Rightarrow x =$ _____

16) $16 = -9 + x \Rightarrow x =$ _____

17) $4x = 28 \Rightarrow x =$ _____

18) $21 = -7x \Rightarrow x =$ _____

19) $12x = -12 \Rightarrow x =$ _____

20) $13x = 39 \Rightarrow x =$ _____

21) $8x = -16 \Rightarrow x =$ _____

22) $\frac{x}{2} = -5 \Rightarrow x =$ _____

23) $\frac{x}{9} = 6 \Rightarrow x =$ _____

24) $27 = \frac{x}{5} \Rightarrow x =$ _____

25) $\frac{x}{4} = -3 \Rightarrow x =$ _____

26) $x \div 8 = 7 \Rightarrow x =$ _____

27) $x \div 2 = -3 \Rightarrow x =$ _____

28) $4x = 48 \Rightarrow x =$ _____

29) $9x = 72 \Rightarrow x =$ _____

30) $8x = -32 \Rightarrow x =$ _____

31) $80 = -10x \Rightarrow x =$ _____

Multi –Step Equations

✎ **Solve each equation.**

1) $3x - 8 = 13 \Rightarrow x = $ ____

2) $23 = -(x - 5) \Rightarrow x = $ ____

3) $-(8 - x) = 15 \Rightarrow x = $ ____

4) $29 = -x + 12 \Rightarrow x = $ ____

5) $2(3 - 2x) = 10 \Rightarrow x = $ ____

6) $3x - 3 = 15 \Rightarrow x = $ ____

7) $32 = -x + 15 \Rightarrow x = $ ____

8) $-(10 - x) = -13 \Rightarrow x = $ ____

9) $-4(7 + x) = 4 \Rightarrow x = $ ____

10) $23 = 2x - 8 \Rightarrow x = $ ____

11) $-6(3 + x) = 6 \Rightarrow x = $ ____

12) $-3 = 3x - 15 \Rightarrow x = $ ____

13) $-7(12 + x) = 7 \Rightarrow x = $ ____

14) $8(6 - 4x) = 16 \Rightarrow x = $ ____

15) $18 - 4x = -9 - x \Rightarrow x = $ ____

16) $6(4 - x) = 30 \Rightarrow x = $ ____

17) $15 - 3x = -5 - x \Rightarrow x = $ ____

18) $9(-7 - 3x) = 18 \Rightarrow x = $ ____

19) $16 - 2x = -4 - 7x \Rightarrow x = $ ____

20) $14 - 2x = 14 + x \Rightarrow x = $ ____

21) $21 - 3x = -7 - 10x \Rightarrow x = $ ___

22) $8 - 2x = 11 + x \Rightarrow x = $ ____

23) $10 + 12x = -8 + 6x \Rightarrow x = $ ____

24) $25 + 20x = -5 + 5x \Rightarrow x = $ ____

25) $16 - x = -8 - 7x \Rightarrow x = $ ____

26) $17 - 3x = 13 + x \Rightarrow x = $ ____

27) $22 + 5x = -8 - x \Rightarrow x = $ ____

28) $-9(7 + x) = 9 \Rightarrow x = $ ____

29) $11 + 3x = -4 - 2x \Rightarrow x = $ ____

30) $13 - 2x = 3 - 3x \Rightarrow x = $ ____

31) $19 - x = -1 - 11x \Rightarrow x = $ ____

32) $12 - 2x = -2 - 4x \Rightarrow x = $ ____

System of Equations

✏️ *Solve each system of equations.*

1) $-x + y = 2$ $\quad x =$
$\quad -2x + y = 3$ $\quad y =$

2) $-5x + y = -3$ $\quad x =$
$\quad 3x - 8y = 24$ $\quad y =$

3) $y = -5$ $\quad x =$
$\quad 4x - 5y = 13$

4) $3y = -6x + 8$ $\quad x =$
$\quad 5x - 4y = -3$ $\quad y =$

5) $10x - 8y = -15$ $\quad x =$
$\quad -6x + 4y = 13$ $\quad y =$

6) $-3x - 4y = 5$ $\quad x =$
$\quad x - 2y = 5$ $\quad y =$

7) $5x - 12y = -19$ $\quad x =$
$\quad -6x + 7y = 8$ $\quad y =$

8) $5x - 7y = -2$ $\quad x =$
$\quad -x - 2y = -3$ $\quad y =$

9) $-x + 3y = 3$ $\quad x =$
$\quad -7x + 8y = -5$ $\quad y =$

10) $-4x + 3y = -18$ $\quad x =$
$\quad 4x - y = 14$ $\quad y =$

11) $6x - 7y = -8$ $\quad x =$
$\quad -x - 4y = -9$ $\quad y =$

12) $-3x + 2y = -16$ $\quad x =$
$\quad 4x - y = 13$ $\quad y =$

13) $-5x + y = -3$ $\quad x =$
$\quad 3x - 8y = 24$ $\quad y =$

14) $3x - 2y = 2$ $\quad x =$
$\quad x - y = 2$ $\quad y =$

15) $4x + 7y = 2$ $\quad x =$
$\quad 6x + 7y = 10$ $\quad y =$

16) $5x + 7y = 18$ $\quad x =$
$\quad -3x + 7y = -22$ $\quad y =$

Graphing Single–Variable Inequalities

 Graph each inequality.

1) $x < 6$

2) $x \geq 1$

3) $x \geq -6$

4) $x \leq -2$

5) $x > -1$

6) $3 > x$

7) $2 \leq x$

8) $x > 0$

9) $-3 \leq x$

10) $-4 \leq x$

11) $x \leq 5$

12) $0 \leq x$

13) $-5 \leq x$

14) $x > -6$

One–Step Inequalities

✎ *Solve each inequality for* x.

1) $x - 10 < 22 \Rightarrow$ _____

2) $18 \leq -4 + x \Rightarrow$ _____

3) $x - 33 > 8 \Rightarrow$ _____

4) $x + 22 \geq 24 \Rightarrow$ _____

5) $x - 24 > 17 \Rightarrow$ _____

6) $x + 5 \geq 3 \Rightarrow x$ _____

7) $x + 14 < 12 \Rightarrow$ _____

8) $26 + x \leq 8 \Rightarrow$ _____

9) $x + 9 \geq -18 \Rightarrow$ _____

10) $x + 24 < 11 \Rightarrow$ _____

11) $17 \leq -5 + x \Rightarrow$ _____

12) $x + 25 > 29 \Rightarrow x$ _____

13) $x - 17 \geq 19 \Rightarrow$ _____

14) $x + 8 > -17 \Rightarrow$ _____

15) $x + 8 < -23 \Rightarrow$ _____

16) $16 \leq -5 + x \Rightarrow$ _____

17) $4x \leq 12 \Rightarrow$ _____

18) $28 \geq -7x \Rightarrow$ _____

19) $2x > -14 \Rightarrow$ _____

20) $13x \leq 39 \Rightarrow$ _____

21) $-8x > -16 \Rightarrow$ _____

22) $\frac{x}{2} < -6 \Rightarrow$ _____

23) $\frac{x}{6} > 6 \Rightarrow$ _____

24) $27 \leq \frac{x}{4} \Rightarrow$ _____

25) $\frac{x}{8} < -3 \Rightarrow$ _____

26) $6x \geq 18 \Rightarrow$ _____

27) $5x \geq -25 \Rightarrow$ _____

28) $4x > 48 \Rightarrow$ _____

29) $8x \leq 72 \Rightarrow$ _____

30) $-4x < -32 \Rightarrow$ _____

31) $40 > -10x \Rightarrow$ _____

Multi –Step Inequalities

✎ *Solve each inequality.*

1) $2x - 8 \leq 8 \rightarrow$ _____

2) $3 + 2x \geq 17 \rightarrow$ _____

3) $5 + 3x \geq 26 \rightarrow$ _____

4) $2x - 8 \leq 14 \rightarrow$ _____

5) $3x - 4 \leq 23 \rightarrow$ _____

6) $7x - 5 \leq 51 \rightarrow$ _____

7) $4x - 9 \leq 27 \rightarrow$ _____

8) $6x - 11 \leq 13 \rightarrow$ _____

9) $5x - 7 \leq 33 \rightarrow$ _____

10) $6 + 2x \geq 28 \rightarrow$ _____

11) $8 + 3x \geq 35 \rightarrow$ _____

12) $4 + 6x < 34 \rightarrow$ _____

13) $3 + 2x \geq 53 \rightarrow$ _____

14) $7 - 6x > 56 + x \rightarrow$ _____

15) $9 + 4x \geq 39 + 2x \rightarrow$ _____

16) $3 + 5x \geq 43 \rightarrow$ _____

17) $4 - 7x < 60 \rightarrow$ _____

18) $11 - 4x \geq 55 \rightarrow$ _____

19) $12 + x \geq 48 - 2x \rightarrow$ _____

20) $10 - 10x \leq -20 \rightarrow$ _____

21) $5 - 9x \geq -40 \rightarrow$ _____

22) $8 - 7x \geq 36 \rightarrow$ _____

23) $5 + 11x < 69 + 3x \rightarrow$ _____

24) $6 + 8x < 28 - 3x \rightarrow$ _____

25) $9 + 11x < 57 - x \rightarrow$ _____

26) $3 + 10x \geq 45 - 4x \rightarrow$ _____

Answers – Chapter 7

One–Step Equations

1) $x = 39$	12) $x = 9$	23) $x = 54$
2) $x = 24$	13) $x = 32$	24) $x = 135$
3) $x = 11$	14) $x = -26$	25) $x = -12$
4) $x = 46$	15) $x = -19$	26) $x = 56$
5) $x = 7$	16) $x = 25$	27) $x = -6$
6) $x = 13$	17) $x = 7$	28) $x = 12$
7) $x = 26$	18) $x = -3$	29) $x = 8$
8) $x = -18$	19) $x = -1$	30) $x = -4$
9) $x = -27$	20) $x = 3$	31) $x = -8$
10) $x = -10$	21) $x = -2$	
11) $x = 22$	22) $x = -10$	

Multi –Step Equations

1) $x = 7$	12) $x = 4$	23) $x = -3$
2) $x = -18$	13) $x = -13$	24) $x = -2$
3) $x = 23$	14) $x = 1$	25) $x = -4$
4) $x = -17$	15) $x = 9$	26) $x = 1$
5) $x = -1$	16) $x = -1$	27) $x = -5$
6) $x = 6$	17) $x = 10$	28) $x = -8$
7) $x = -17$	18) $x = -3$	29) $x = -3$
8) $x = -3$	19) $x = -4$	30) $x = -10$
9) $x = -8$	20) $x = 0$	31) $x = -2$
10) $x = 15$	21) $x = -4$	32) $x = -7$
11) $x = -4$	22) $x = -1$	

System of Equations

1) $x = -1, y = 1$	9) $x = 3 , y = 2$
2) $x = 0 , y = -3$	10) $x = 3 , y = -2$
3) $x = -3$	11) $x = 1, y = 2$
4) $x = 1 , y = 2$	12) $x = 2, y = -5$
5) $x = -\frac{11}{2} , y = -5$	13) $x = 0, y = -3$
6) $x = 1 , y = -2$	14) $x = -2, y = -4$
7) $x = 1 , y = 2$	15) $x = 4, y = -2$
8) $x = 1 , y = 1$	16) $x = 5 , y = -1$

Graphing Single–Variable Inequalities

1) $x < 6$

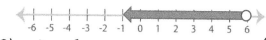

2) $x \geq 1$

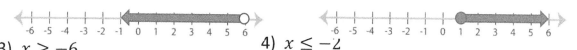

3) $x \geq -6$

4) $x \leq -2$

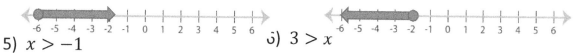

5) $x > -1$

6) $3 > x$

7) $2 \leq x$

8) $x > 0$

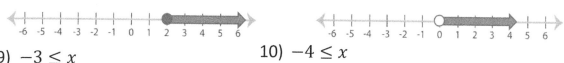

9) $-3 \leq x$

10) $-4 \leq x$

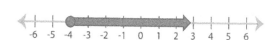

11) $x \leq 5$

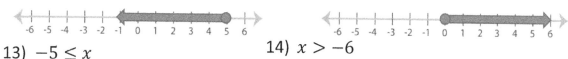

12) $0 \leq x$

13) $-5 \leq x$

14) $x > -6$

One–Step Inequalities

1) $x < 32$
2) $22 \leq x$
3) $41 \leq x$
4) $x \geq 2$
5) $x > 41$
6) $x \geq -2$
7) $x < -2$
8) $x \leq -18$
9) $x \geq -27$
10) $x < -13$

11) $22 \leq x$
12) $x > 4$
13) $x \geq 36$
14) $x > -25$
15) $x < -31$
16) $21 \leq x$
17) $x \leq 3$
18) $-4 \leq x$
19) $x > -7$
20) $x \leq 3$
21) $x < 2$

22) $x < -12$
23) $x > 36$
24) $108 \leq x$
25) $x < -24$
26) $x \geq 3$
27) $x \geq -5$
28) $x > 12$
29) $x \leq 9$
30) $x > 8$
31) $-4 < x$

Multi –Step Inequalities

1) $x \leq 8$
2) $x \geq 7$
3) $x \geq 7$
4) $x \leq 11$
5) $x \leq 9$
6) $x \leq 8$
7) $x \leq 9$
8) $x \leq 4$
9) $x \leq 8$

10) $x \geq 11$
11) $x \geq 9$
12) $x < 5$
13) $x \geq 25$
14) $x < -7$
15) $x \geq 15$
16) $x \geq 8$
17) $x > -8$
18) $x \leq -11$

19) $x \geq 12$
20) $x \geq 3$
21) $x \leq 5$
22) $x \leq -4$
23) $x < 8$
24) $x < 2$
25) $x < 4$
26) $x \geq 3$

Chapter 8:

Exponents and Variables

Math Topics that you'll learn in this Chapter:

- ✓ Multiplication Property of Exponents

- ✓ Division Property of Exponents

- ✓ Powers of Products and Quotients

- ✓ Zero and Negative Exponents

- ✓ Negative Exponents and Negative Bases

- ✓ Scientific Notation

- ✓ Radicals

Multiplication Property of Exponents

✎ *Simplify and write the answer in exponential form.*

1) $2 \times 2^2 =$

2) $5^3 \times 5 =$

3) $3^2 \times 3^2 =$

4) $4^2 \times 4^2 =$

5) $7^3 \times 7^2 \times 7 =$

6) $2 \times 2^2 \times 2^2 =$

7) $5^3 \times 5^2 \times 5 \times 5 =$

8) $2x \times x =$

9) $x^3 \times x^2 =$

10) $x^4 \times x^4 =$

11) $x^2 \times x^2 \times x^2 =$

12) $6x \times 6x =$

13) $2x^2 \times 2x^2 =$

14) $3x^2 \times x =$

15) $4x^4 \times 4x^4 \times 4x^4 =$

16) $2x^2 \times x^2 =$

17) $x^4 \times 3x =$

18) $x \times 2x^2 =$

19) $5x^4 \times 5x^4 =$

20) $2yx^2 \times 2x =$

21) $3x^4 \times y^2x^4 =$

22) $y^2x^3 \times y^5x^2 =$

23) $4yx^3 \times 2x^2y^3 =$

24) $6x^2 \times 6x^3y^4 =$

25) $3x^4y^5 \times 7x^2y^3 =$

26) $7x^2y^5 \times 9xy^3 =$

27) $7xy^4 \times 4x^3y^3 =$

28) $3x^5y^3 \times 8x^2y^3 =$

29) $3x \times y^5x^3 \times y^4 =$

30) $yx^2 \times 2y^2x^2 \times 2xy =$

31) $4yx^4 \times 5y^5x \times xy^3 =$

32) $7x^2 \times 10x^3y^3 \times 8yx^4 =$

Division Property of Exponents

✎ *Simplify and write the answer.*

1) $\dfrac{2^2}{2^3} =$

2) $\dfrac{2^4}{2^2} =$

3) $\dfrac{5^5}{5} =$

4) $\dfrac{3}{3^5} =$

5) $\dfrac{x}{x^3} =$

6) $\dfrac{3 \times 3^3}{3^2 \times 3^4} =$

7) $\dfrac{5^8}{5^3} =$

8) $\dfrac{5 \times 5^6}{5^2 \times 5^7} =$

9) $\dfrac{3^4 \times 3^7}{3^2 \times 3^8} =$

10) $\dfrac{5x}{10x^3} =$

11) $\dfrac{5x^3}{2x^5} =$

12) $\dfrac{18x^3}{14^{\ 6}} =$

13) $\dfrac{12x^3}{8xy^8} =$

14) $\dfrac{24xy^3}{4x^4y^2} =$

15) $\dfrac{21^{\ 3}y^9}{7xy^5} =$

16) $\dfrac{36x^2y^9}{4x^3} =$

17) $\dfrac{12^{\ 4}y^4}{10x^6y^7} =$

18) $\dfrac{12^{\ 2}x^{12}}{20yx^8} =$

19) $\dfrac{16x^4y}{9x^8y^2} =$

20) $\dfrac{5x^8y^2}{20^{\ 5}y^5} =$

Powers of Products and Quotients

🖎 *Simplify and write the answer.*

1) $(4^2)^2 =$

2) $(6^2)^3 =$

3) $(2 \times 2^3)^4 =$

4) $(4 \times 4^4)^2 =$

5) $(3^3 \times 3^2)^3 =$

6) $(5^4 \times 5^5)^2 =$

7) $(2 \times 2^4)^2 =$

8) $(2x^6)^2 =$

9) $(11x^5)^2 =$

10) $(4x^2y^4)^4 =$

11) $(2x^4y^4)^3 =$

12) $(3x^2y^2)^2 =$

13) $(3x^4y^3)^4 =$

14) $(2x^6y^8)^2 =$

15) $(12x^3x)^3 =$

16) $(5x^9x^6)^3 =$

17) $(5x^{10}y^3)^3 =$

18) $(14x^3x^3)^2 =$

19) $(3x^3 . 5x)^2 =$

20) $(10x^{11}y^3)^2 =$

21) $(9x^7y^5)^2 =$

22) $(4x^4y^6)^5 =$

23) $(3x . 4y^3)^2 =$

24) $\left(\frac{6x}{x^2}\right)^2 =$

25) $\left(\frac{x^5y^5}{x^2y^2}\right)^3 =$

26) $\left(\frac{24x}{4x^6}\right)^2 =$

27) $\left(\frac{x^5}{x^7y^2}\right)^2 =$

28) $\left(\frac{xy^2}{x^2y^3}\right)^3 =$

29) $\left(\frac{4xy^4}{x^5}\right)^2 =$

30) $\left(\frac{xy^4}{5xy^2}\right)^3 =$

Zero and Negative Exponents

✎ *Evaluate the following expressions.*

1) $1^{-1} =$

2) $2^{-2} =$

3) $0^{15} =$

4) $1^{-10} =$

5) $8^{-1} =$

6) $8^{-2} =$

7) $2^{-4} =$

8) $10^{-2} =$

9) $9^{-2} =$

10) $3^{-3} =$

11) $7^{-3} =$

12) $3^{-4} =$

13) $6^{-3} =$

14) $5^{-3} =$

15) $22^{-1=}$

16) $4^{-4} =$

17) $5^{-4} =$

18) $15^{-2} =$

19) $4^{-5} =$

20) $9^{-3} =$

21) $3^{-5} =$

22) $5^{-4} =$

23) $12^{-3} =$

24) $15^{-3} =$

25) $20^{-3} =$

26) $50^{-2} =$

27) $18^{-3} =$

28) $24^{-2} =$

29) $30^{-3} =$

30) $10^{-5} =$

31) $\left(\frac{1}{8}\right)^{-1}$

32) $\left(\frac{1}{5}\right)^{-2} =$

33) $\left(\frac{1}{7}\right)^{-2} =$

34) $\left(\frac{2}{3}\right)^{-2} =$

35) $\left(\frac{1}{5}\right)^{-3} =$

36) $\left(\frac{3}{4}\right)^{-2} =$

37) $\left(\frac{2}{5}\right)^{-2} =$

38) $\left(\frac{1}{2}\right)^{-8} =$

39) $\left(\frac{2}{5}\right)^{-3} =$

40) $\left(\frac{3}{7}\right)^{-2} =$

41) $\left(\frac{5}{6}\right)^{-3} =$

42) $\left(\frac{4}{9}\right)^{-2} =$

Negative Exponents and Negative Bases

✍ *Simplify and write the answer.*

1) $-3^{-1} =$

2) $-5^{-2} =$

3) $-2^{-4} =$

4) $-x^{-3} =$

5) $2x^{-1} =$

6) $-4x^{-3} =$

7) $-12x^{-5} =$

8) $-5x^{-2}y^{-3} =$

9) $20x^{-4}y^{-1} =$

10) $14a^{-6}b^{-7} =$

11) $-12x^2y^{-3} =$

12) $-\dfrac{25}{x^{-6}} =$

13) $-\dfrac{2x}{a^{-4}} =$

14) $\left(-\dfrac{1}{3x}\right)^{-2} =$

15) $\left(-\dfrac{3}{4x}\right)^{-2} =$

16) $-\dfrac{9}{a^{-7}b^{-2}} =$

17) $-\dfrac{5x}{x^{-3}} =$

18) $-\dfrac{a^{-3}}{b^{-2}} =$

19) $-\dfrac{8}{x^{-3}} =$

20) $\dfrac{5b}{-9c^{-4}} =$

21) $\dfrac{9ab}{a^{-3}b^{-1}} =$

22) $-\dfrac{15a^{-2}}{30b^{-3}} =$

23) $\dfrac{4ab^{-2}}{-3c^{-2}} =$

24) $\left(\dfrac{3a}{2c}\right)^{-2} =$

25) $\left(-\dfrac{5x}{3yz}\right)^{-3} =$

26) $\dfrac{11ab^{-2}}{-3c^{-2}} =$

27) $\left(-\dfrac{x^3}{x^4}\right)^{-2} =$

28) $\left(-\dfrac{x^{-2}}{3x^2}\right)^{-3} =$

Scientific Notation

✍ **Write each number in scientific notation.**

1) 0.113 =

2) 0.02 =

3) 7.5 =

4) 20 =

5) 60 =

6) 0.004 =

7) 78 =

8) 1,600 =

9) 1,450 =

10) 31,000 =

11) 2,000,000 =

12) 0.0000003 =

13) 554,000 =

14) 0.000725 =

15) 0.00034 =

16) 86,000,000 =

17) 62,000 =

18) 97,000,000 =

19) 0.0000045 =

20) 0.0019 =

✍ **Write each number in standard notation.**

21) 2×10^{-1} =

22) 8×10^{-2} =

23) 1.8×10^3 =

24) 9×10^{-4} =

25) 1.7×10^{-2} =

26) 9×10^3 =

27) 7×10^5 =

28) 1.15×10^4 =

29) 7×10^{-5} =

30) 8.3×10^{-5} =

Radicals

🖎 *Simplify and write the answer.*

1) $\sqrt{0} =$ _____

2) $\sqrt{1} =$ _____

3) $\sqrt{4} =$ _____

4) $\sqrt{16} =$ _____

5) $\sqrt{9} =$ _____

6) $\sqrt{25} =$ _____

7) $\sqrt{49} =$ _____

8) $\sqrt{36} =$ _____

9) $\sqrt{64} =$ _____

10) $\sqrt{81} =$ _____

11) $\sqrt{121} =$ _____

12) $\sqrt{225} =$ _____

13) $\sqrt{144} =$ _____

14) $\sqrt{100} =$ _____

15) $\sqrt{256} =$ _____

16) $\sqrt{289} =$ _____

17) $\sqrt{324} =$ _____

18) $\sqrt{400} =$ _____

19) $\sqrt{900} =$ _____

20) $\sqrt{529} =$ _____

21) $\sqrt{361} =$ _____

22) $\sqrt{169} =$ _____

23) $\sqrt{196} =$ _____

24) $\sqrt{90} =$ _____

🖎 *Evaluate.*

25) $\sqrt{6} \times \sqrt{6} =$

26) $\sqrt{5} \times \sqrt{5} =$

27) $\sqrt{8} \times \sqrt{8} =$

28) $\sqrt{2} + \sqrt{2} =$

29) $\sqrt{8} + \sqrt{8} =$

30) $6\sqrt{5} - 2\sqrt{5} =$

31) $\sqrt{25} \times \sqrt{16} =$

32) $\sqrt{25} \times \sqrt{64} =$

33) $\sqrt{81} \times \sqrt{25} =$

34) $5\sqrt{3} \times 2\sqrt{3} =$

35) $8\sqrt{2} \times 2\sqrt{2} =$

36) $6\sqrt{3} - \sqrt{12} =$

Answers – Chapter 8

Multiplication Property of Exponents

1) 2^3

2) 5^4

3) 3^4

4) 4^4

5) 7^6

6) 2^5

7) 5^7

8) $2x^2$

9) x^5

10) x^8

11) x^6

12) $36x^2$

13) $4x^4$

14) $3x^3$

15) $64x^{12}$

16) $2x^4$

17) $3x^5$

18) $2x^3$

19) $25x^8$

20) $4x^3y$

21) $3x^8y^2$

22) x^5y^7

23) $8x^5y^4$

24) $36x^5y^4$

25) $21x^6y^8$

26) $63x^3y^8$

27) $28x^4y^7$

28) $24x^7y^6$

29) $3x^4y^9$

30) $4x^5y^4$

31) $20x^6y^9$

32) $560x^9y^4$

Division Property of Exponents

1) $\frac{1}{2}$

2) 2^2

3) 5^4

4) $\frac{1}{3^4}$

5) $\frac{1}{x^2}$

6) $\frac{1}{3}$

7) 5^5

8) $\frac{1}{5^2}$

9) 3

10) $\frac{1}{2x^2}$

11) $\frac{5}{2x^2}$

12) $\frac{9}{7x^3}$

13) $\frac{3x^2}{2y^8}$

14) $\frac{6y}{x^3}$

15) $3x^2y^4$

16) $\frac{9y^9}{x}$

17) $\frac{6}{5x^2y^3}$

18) $\frac{3yx^4}{5}$

19) $\frac{16}{9x^4y}$

20) $\frac{x^3}{4y^3}$

Powers of Products and Quotients

1) 4^4

2) 6^6

3) 2^{16}

4) 4^{10}

5) 3^{15}

6) 5^{18}

7) 2^{10}

8) $4x^{12}$

9) $121x^{10}$

10) $256x^8y^{16}$

11) $8x^{12}y^{12}$

12) $9x^4y^4$

13) $81x^{16}y^{12}$

14) $4x^{12}y^{16}$

15) $1,728x^{12}$

16) $125x^{45}$

17) $125x^{30}y^9$

18) $196x^{12}$

19) $225x^8$

20) $100x^{22}y^6$

21) $81x^{14}y^{10}$

22) $1,024x^{20}y^{30}$

23) $144x^2y^6$

24) $\frac{36}{x^2}$

25) x^9y^9

26) $\frac{36}{x^{10}}$

27) $\frac{1}{x^4 y^4}$

28) $\frac{1}{x^3 y^3}$

29) $\frac{16y^8}{x^8}$

30) $\frac{y^6}{125}$

Zero and Negative Exponents

1) 1

2) $\frac{1}{4}$

3) 0

4) 1

5) $\frac{1}{8}$

6) $\frac{1}{64}$

7) $\frac{1}{16}$

8) $\frac{1}{100}$

9) $\frac{1}{81}$

10) $\frac{1}{27}$

11) $\frac{1}{343}$

12) $\frac{1}{81}$

13) $\frac{1}{216}$

14) $\frac{1}{125}$

15) $\frac{1}{22}$

16) $\frac{1}{256}$

17) $\frac{1}{625}$

18) $\frac{1}{225}$

19) $\frac{1}{1,024}$

20) $\frac{1}{729}$

21) $\frac{1}{243}$

22) $\frac{1}{625}$

23) $\frac{1}{144}$

24) $\frac{1}{3,375}$

25) $\frac{1}{8,000}$

26) $\frac{1}{2,500}$

27) $\frac{1}{5,832}$

28) $\frac{1}{576}$

29) $\frac{1}{27,000}$

30) $\frac{1}{100,000}$

31) 8

32) 25

33) 49

34) $\frac{9}{4}$

35) 125

36) $\frac{64}{27}$

37) $\frac{25}{4}$

38) 256

39) $\frac{125}{8}$

40) $\frac{49}{9}$

41) $\frac{216}{125}$

42) $\frac{81}{16}$

Negative Exponents and Negative Bases

1) $-\frac{1}{3}$

2) $-\frac{1}{25}$

3) $-\frac{1}{16}$

4) $-\frac{1}{x^3}$

5) $\frac{2}{x}$

6) $-\frac{4}{x^3}$

7) $-\frac{12}{x^5}$

8) $-\frac{5}{x^2 y^3}$

9) $\frac{20}{x^4 y}$

10) $\frac{14}{a^6 b^7}$

11) $-\frac{12x^2}{y^3}$

12) $-25x^6$

13) $-2xa^4$

14) $9x^2$

15) $\frac{16x^2}{9}$

16) $-9a^7 b^2$

17) $-5x^4$

18) $-\frac{b^2}{a^3}$

19) $-8x^3$

20) $-\frac{5bc^4}{9}$

21) $9a^4 b^2$

22) $-\frac{b^3}{2a^2}$

23) $-\frac{4ac^2}{3b^2}$

24) $\frac{4c^2}{9a^2}$

25) $-\frac{27\ ^3 z^3}{125x^3}$

26) $-\frac{11ac^2}{3b^2}$

27) x^2

28) $-27x^{12}$

Scientific Notation

1) 1.13×10^{-1}
2) 2×10^{-2}
3) 2.5×10^{0}
4) 2×10^{1}
5) 6×10^{1}
6) 4×10^{-3}
7) 7.8×10^{1}
8) 1.6×10^{3}
9) 1.45×10^{3}
10) 3.1×10^{4}
20) 1.9×10^{-3}

11) 2×10^{6}
12) 3×10^{-7}
13) 5.54×10^{5}
14) 7.25×10^{-4}
15) 3.4×10^{-4}
16) 8.6×10^{7}
17) 6.2×10^{4}
18) 9.7×10^{7}
19) 4.5×10^{-6}

21) $= 0.2$
22) 0.08
23) 1,800
24) 0.0009
25) 0.017

26) 9,000
27) 700,000
28) 11,500
29) 0.00007
30) 0.000083

Radicals

1) 0
2) 1
3) 2
4) 4
5) 3
6) 5
7) 7
8) 6

9) 8
10) 9
11) 11
12) 15
13) 12
14) 10
15) 16
16) 17

17) 18
18) 20
19) 30
20) 23
21) 19
22) 13
23) 14
24) $3\sqrt{10}$

25) 6
26) 5
27) 8
28) $2\sqrt{2}$

29) $2\sqrt{8} = 4\sqrt{2}$
30) $4\sqrt{5}$
31) 20
32) 40

33) 45
34) 30
35) 32
36) $4\sqrt{3}$

Chapter 9:

Geometry and Solid Figures

Math Topics that you'll learn in this Chapter:

- ✓ The Pythagorean Theorem
- ✓ Triangles
- ✓ Polygons
- ✓ Circles
- ✓ Trapezoids
- ✓ Cubes
- ✓ Rectangle Prisms
- ✓ Cylinder

The Pythagorean Theorem

✍ *Do the following lengths form a right triangle?*

1) _____
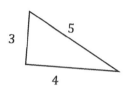

2) _____
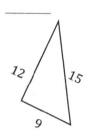

3) _____
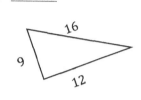

4) _____
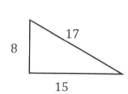

5) _____

6) _____
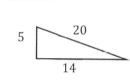

7) _____
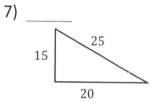

8) _____
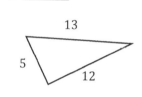

✍ *Find the missing side.*

9) _____
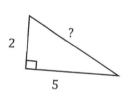

10) _____
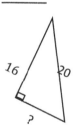

11) _____
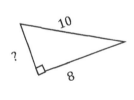

12) _____
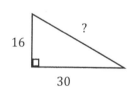

13) _____

14) _____

15) _____
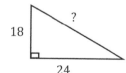

16) _____
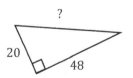

Triangles

✍ *Find the measure of the unknown angle in each triangle.*

1) _____

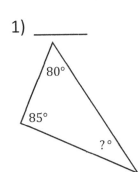

2) _____

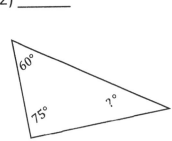

3) _____

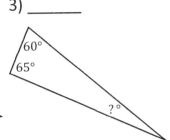

4) _____

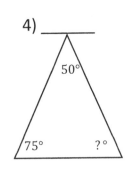

5) _____

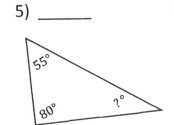

6) _____

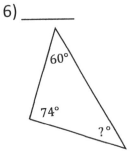

7) _____

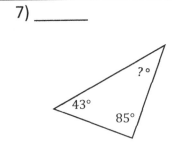

8) _____

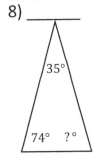

✍ *Find area of each triangle.*

9) _____

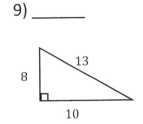

10) _____

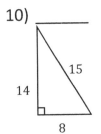

11) _____

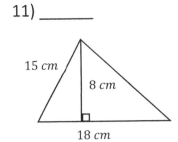

12) _____

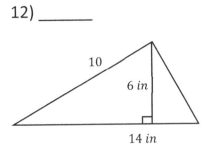

SSAT Middle Level Math Workbook 2020 - 2021

Polygons

✎ *Find the perimeter of each shape.*

1) (square) _____

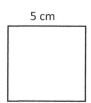
5 cm

2) _____

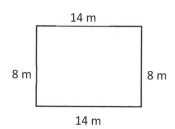
14 m
8 m   8 m
14 m

3) _____

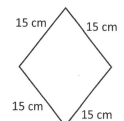
15 cm   15 cm
15 cm   15 cm

4) (square) _____

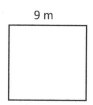
9 m

5) *(regular hexagon* _____

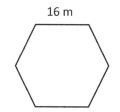
16 m

6) _____

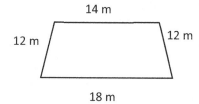
14 m
12 m   12 m
18 m

7) *(parallelogram* _____

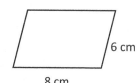
6 cm
8 cm

8) *(regular hexagon)* _____

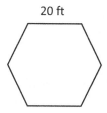
20 ft

9) _____

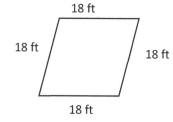
18 ft
18 ft   18 ft
18 ft

10) _____

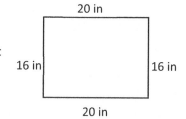
20 in
16 in   16 in
20 in

11) _____

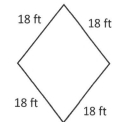
18 ft   18 ft
18 ft   18 ft

12) *(regular hexagon)* _____

32 in

Circles

✏️ **Find the Circumference of each circle.** (π = 3.14)

1) ____ 2) ____ 3) ____ 4) ____ 5) ____ 6) ____

7 in 12 cm 14 ft 13 m 18 cm 15 miles

7) ____ 8) ____ 9) ____ 10) ____ 11) ____ 12) ____

19 in 22 ft 25 m 28 cm 35 miles 50 ft

✏️ **Complete the table below.** (π = 3.14)

	Radius	Diameter	Circumference	Area
Circle 1	2 inches	4 inches	12.56 inches	12.56 square inches
Circle 2		8 meters		
Circle 3				113.04 square ft
Circle 4			50.24 miles	
Circle 5		9 km		
Circle 6	7 cm			
Circle 7		10 feet		
Circle 8				615.44 square meters
Circle 9			81.64 inches	
Circle 10	12 feet			

Cubes

✍ *Find the volume of each cube.*

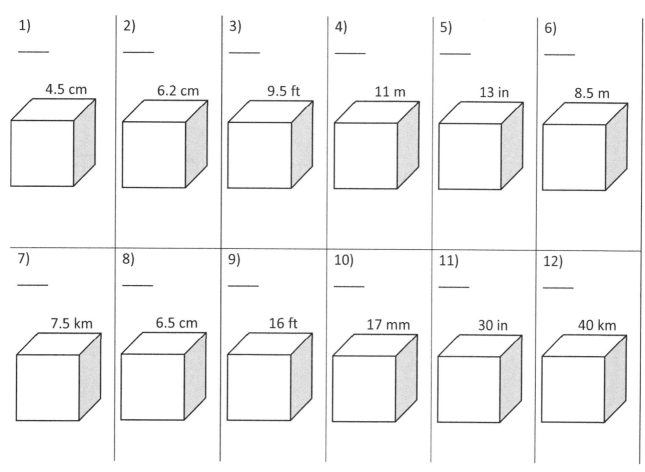

1) ___
4.5 cm

2) ___
6.2 cm

3) ___
9.5 ft

4) ___
11 m

5) ___
13 in

6) ___
8.5 m

7) ___
7.5 km

8) ___
6.5 cm

9) ___
16 ft

10) ___
17 mm

11) ___
30 in

12) ___
40 km

✍ *Find the surface area of each cube.*

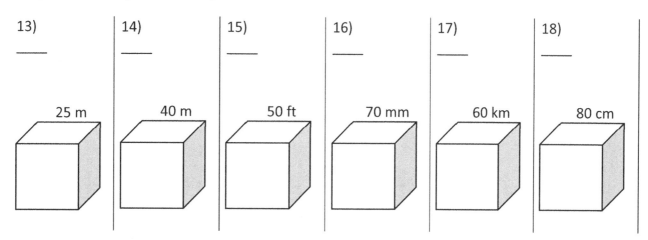

13) ___
25 m

14) ___
40 m

15) ___
50 ft

16) ___
70 mm

17) ___
60 km

18) ___
80 cm

Trapezoids

✍ *Find the area of each trapezoid.*

1) _____

10 cm
8 cm
16 cm

2) _____

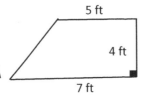
14 m
10 m
18 m

3) _____

5 ft
4 ft
7 ft

4) _____

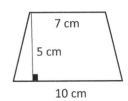
7 cm
5 cm
10 cm

5) _____

4 cm
6 cm
12 cm

6) _____

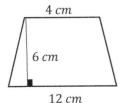
12 in
8 in
16 in

7) _____

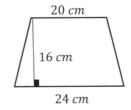
20 cm
16 cm
24 cm

8) _____

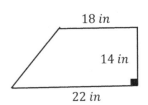
18 in
14 in
22 in

✍ *Solve.*

9) A trapezoid has an area of 80 cm² and its height is 8 cm and one base is 12 cm. What is the other base length? _____

10) If a trapezoid has an area of 120 ft² and the lengths of the bases are 14 ft and 16 ft, find the height. _____

11) If a trapezoid has an area of 160 m² and its height is 10 m and one base is 14 m, find the other base length. _____

12) The area of a trapezoid is 504 ft² and its height is 24 ft. If one base of the trapezoid is 14 ft, what is the other base length? _____

Rectangular Prisms

✎ *Find the volume of each Rectangular Prism.*

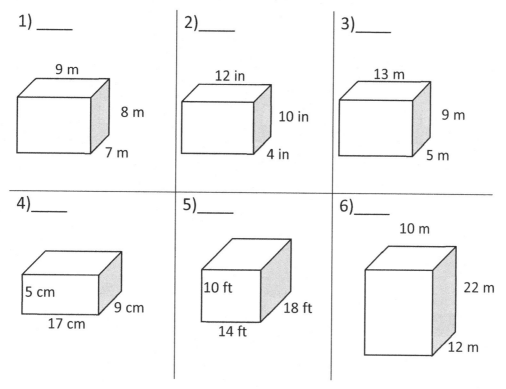

1) ____

9 m
8 m
7 m

2) ____

12 in
10 in
4 in

3) ____

13 m
9 m
5 m

4) ____

5 cm
9 cm
17 cm

5) ____

10 ft
18 ft
14 ft

6) ____

10 m
22 m
12 m

✎ *Find the surface area of each Rectangular Prism.*

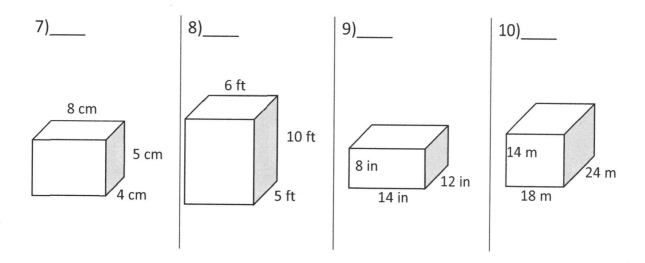

7) ____

8 cm
5 cm
4 cm

8) ____

6 ft
10 ft
5 ft

9) ____

8 in
12 in
14 in

10) ____

14 m
24 m
18 m

Cylinder

✍ *Find the volume of each Cylinder.* (π = 3.14)

1) _____
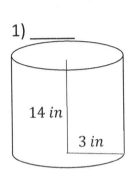
14 in
3 in

2) _____
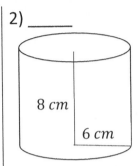
8 cm
6 cm

3) _____
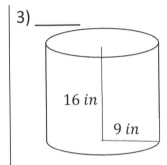
16 in
9 in

4) _____
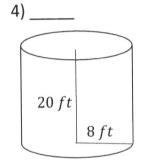
20 ft
8 ft

5) _____
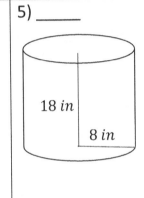
18 in
8 in

6) _____
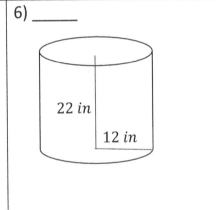
22 in
12 in

✍ *Find the surface area of each Cylinder.* (π = 3.14)

7) _____
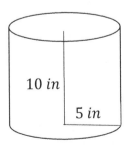
10 in
5 in

8) _____
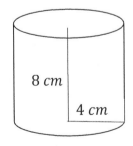
8 cm
4 cm

9) _____
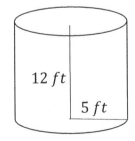
12 ft
5 ft

10) _____
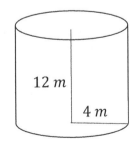
12 m
4 m

SSAT Middle Level Math Workbook 2020 - 2021

Answers – Chapter 9

The Pythagorean Theorem

1) *yes*
2) *yes*
3) *no*
4) *yes*
5) *no*
6) *no*
7) *yes*
8) *yes*
9) 51
10) 12
11) 6
12) 34
13) 26
14) 13
15) 30
16) 52

Triangles

1) 15°
2) 45°
3) 55°
4) 55°
5) 45°
6) 46°
7) 52°
8) 71°
9) 40
10) 56
11) 72 cm^2
12) 42 in^2

Polygons

1) 20 *cm*
2) 44 *m*
3) 60 *cm*
4) 36 *m*
5) 96 *m*
6) 56 *m*
7) 28 *cm*
8) 120 *ft*
9) 72 *ft*
10) 72 *in*
11) 88 *ft*
12) 192 *in*

Circles

1) 43.96 *in*
2) 75.36 *cm*
3) 87.92 *ft*
4) 81.64 *m*
5) 113.04 *cm*
6) 94.2 *miles*
7) 119.32 *in*
8) 138.16 *ft*
9) 157 *m*
10) 175.84 *m*
11) 219.8 *in*
12) 314 *ft*

	Radius	Diameter	Circumference	Area
Circle 1	2 inches	4 inches	12.56 inches	12.56 square inches
Circle 2	4 meters	8 meters	25.12 meters	50.24 square meters
Circle 3	6 ft	12 ft	37.68	113.04 square ft
Circle 4	8 miles	16 miles	50.24 miles	200.96 square miles
Circle 5	4.5 km	9 km	28.26 km	63.585 square km
Circle 6	7 cm	14 cm	43.96 cm	153.86 square cm
Circle 7	5 feet	10 feet	31.4 feet	78.5 square feet
Circle 8	14 m	28 m	87.92 m	615.44 square meters
Circle 9	13 in	26 in	81.64 inches	530.66 square inches
Circle 10	12 feet	24 feet	75.36 feet	452.16 square feet

Cubes

1) $91.125\ cm^3$
2) $238.328\ cm^3$
3) $857.375\ ft^3$
4) $1{,}331\ m^3$
5) $2{,}197\ in^3$
6) $614.125\ m^3$
7) $421.875\ km^3$
8) $274.625\ cm^3$
9) $4{,}096\ ft^3$

10) $4{,}913\ \ cm^3$
11) $27{,}000\ in^3$
12) $64{,}000\ km^3$
13) $3{,}750\ m^2$
14) $9{,}600\ m^2$
15) $15{,}000\ ft^2$
16) $29{,}400\ mm^2$
17) $21{,}600\ km^2$
18) $38{,}400\ cm^2$

Trapezoids

1) $104\ cm^2$
2) $160\ m^2$
3) $224\ ft^2$
4) $324\ cm^2$
5) $288\ cm^2$
6) $414\ in^2$

7) $448\ cm^2$
8) $528\ in^2$
9) $8\ cm$
10) $8\ ft$
11) $18\ m$
12) $28\ ft$

Rectangular Prisms

1) $504\ m^3$
2) $480\ in^3$
3) $585\ m^3$
4) $765\ cm^3$
5) $2{,}520\ ft^3$

6) $2{,}640\ m^3$
7) $184\ cm^2$
8) $280\ ft^2$
9) $752\ in^2$
10) $2{,}040\ m^2$

Cylinder

1) $395.64\ in^3$
2) $904.32\ cm^3$
3) $4{,}069.44\ in^3$
4) $4{,}019.2\ ft^3$
5) $3{,}617.28\ in^3$

6) $9{,}947.52\ in^3$
7) $471\ in^2$
8) $301.44\ cm^2$
9) $533.8\ ft^2$
10) $401.92\ m^2$

Chapter 10:

Statistics

Math Topics that you'll learn in this Chapter:

✓ Mean, Median, Mode, and Range of the Given Data

✓ Pie Graph

✓ Probability Problems

✓ Permutations and Combinations

Mean, Median, Mode, and Range of the Given Data

✍️ *Find the values of the Given Data.*

1) 6, 12, 1, 1, 5

Mode: _____   Range: _____

Mean: _____   Median: _____

2) 5, 8, 3, 7, 4, 3

Mode: _____   Range: _____

Mean: _____   Median: _____

3) 12, 5, 8, 7, 8

Mode: _____   Range: _____

Mean: _____   Median: _____

4) 8, 4, 10, 7, 3, 4

Mode: _____   Range: _____

Mean: _____   Median: _____

5) 9, 7, 10, 5, 7, 4, 14

Mode: _____   Range: _____

Mean: _____   Median: _____

6) 8, 1, 6, 6, 9, 2, 17

Mode: _____   Range: _____

Mean: _____   Median: _____

7) 12, 6, 1, 7, 9, 7, 8, 14

Mode: _____   Range: _____

Mean: _____   Median: _____

8) 10, 14, 5, 4, 11, 6, 13

Mode: _____   Range: _____

Mean: _____   Median: _____

9) 16, 15, 15, 16, 13, 14, 23

Mode: _____   Range: _____

Mean: _____   Median: _____

10) 16, 15, 12, 8, 4, 9, 8, 16

Mode: _____   Range: _____

Mean: _____   Median: _____

Pie Graph

✎ *The circle graph below shows all Wilson's expenses for last month. Wilson spent $200 on his bills last month.*

Answer following questions based on the Pie graph.

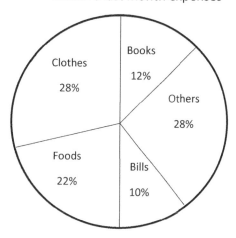

Wilson's last month expenses

1) How much was Wilson's total expenses last month? _____

2) How much did Wilson spend on his clothes last month? _____

3) How much did Wilson spend for foods last month? _____

4) How much did Wilson spend on his books last month? _____

5) What fraction is Wilson's expenses for his bills and clothes out of his total

   expenses last month? _____

Probability Problems

1) If there are 10 red balls and 20 blue balls in a basket, what is the probability that Oliver will pick out a red ball from the basket? _____

Gender	Under 45	45 or older	total
Male	12	6	18
Female	5	7	12
Total	17	13	30

2) The table above shows the distribution of age and gender for 30 employees in a company. If one employee is selected at random, what is the probability that the employee selected be either a female under age 45 or a male age 45 or older? _____

3) A number is chosen at random from 1 to 18. Find the probability of not selecting a composite number. (A composite number is a number that is divisible by itself, 1 and at least one other whole number) _____

4) There are 6 blue marbles, 8 red marbles, and 5 yellow marbles in a box. If Ava randomly selects a marble from the box, what is the probability of selecting a red or yellow marble? _____

5) A bag contains 19 balls: three green, five black, eight blue, a brown, a red and one white. If 18 balls are removed from the bag at random, what is the probability that a brown ball has been removed? _____

6) There are only red and blue marbles in a box. The probability of choosing a red marble in the box at random is one fourth. If there are 132 blue marbles, how many marbles are in the box? _____

Permutations and Combinations

✍ *Calculate the value of each.*

1) $5! = $ ____

2) $6! = $ ____

3) $8! = $ ____

4) $5! + 6! = $ ____

5) $8! + 3! = $ ____

6) $6! + 7! = $ ____

7) $8! + 4! = $ ____

8) $9! - 3! = $ ____

✍ *Solve each word problems.*

9) Sophia is baking cookies. She uses milk, flour and eggs. How many different orders of ingredients can she try? _____

10) William is planning for his vacation. He wants to go to restaurant, watch a movie, go to the beach, and play basketball. How many different ways of ordering are there for him? _____

11) How many 7-digit numbers can be named using the digits 1, 2, 3, 4, 5, 6 and 7 without repetition? _____

12) In how many ways can 9 boys be arranged in a straight line? _____

13) In how many ways can 10 athletes be arranged in a straight line? _____

14) A professor is going to arrange her 7 students in a straight line. In how many ways can she do this? _____

15) How many code symbols can be formed with the letters for the word BLACK? _____

16) In how many ways a team of 7 basketball players can choose a captain and co-captain? _____

Answers – Chapter 10

Mean, Median, Mode, and Range of the Given Data

1) Mode: 1   Range: 11   Mean: 5   Median: 5
2) Mode: 3   Range: 5   Mean: 5   Median: 4.5
3) Mode: 8   Range: 7   Mean: 8   Median: 8
4) Mode: 4   Range: 7   Mean: 6   Median: 5.5
5) Mode: 7   Range: 10   Mean: 8   Median: 7
6) Mode: 6   Range: 16   Mean: 7   Median: 6
7) Mode: 7   Range: 13   Mean: 8   Median: 7.5
8) Mode: *no mode*   Range: 10   Mean: 9   Median: 10
9) Mode: 15 *and* 16   Range: 10   Mean: 16   Median: 15
10) Mode: 8 *and* 16   Range: 12   Mean: 11   Median: 10.5

Pie Graph

1) $2,000
2) $560
3) $440
4) $240
5) $\frac{19}{50}$

Probability Problems

1) $\frac{1}{3}$
2) $\frac{11}{30}$
3) $\frac{7}{18}$
4) $\frac{13}{19}$
5) $\frac{18}{19}$
6) 176

Permutations and Combinations

1) 120
2) 720
3) 40,320
4) 840
5) 40,326
6) 5,760
7) 40,344
8) 362,874
9) *6*
10) *24*
11) 5,040
12) 362,880
13) 3,628,800
14) 5,040
15) 120
16) 42

SSAT Middle Level Test Review

The SSAT, or Secondary School Admissions Test, is a standardized test to help determine admission to private elementary, middle and high schools.

There are currently three Levels of the SSAT:

- ✓ Lower Level (for students in 3rd and 4th grade)
- ✓ Middle Level (for students in 5th-7th grade)
- ✓ Upper Level (for students in 8th-11th grade)

There are six sections on the SSAT Middle Level Test:

- ✓ Writing: 25 minutes.
- ✓ Math section: 25 questions, 30 minutes
- ✓ Reading section: 40 questions, 40 minutes
- ✓ Verbal section: 60 questions, 30 minutes
- ✓ Math section: 25 questions, 30 minutes
- ✓ Experimental: 16 questions, 15 minutes.

In this book, there are 2 complete SSAT Middle Level Math Practice Tests. Take these tests to see what score you'll be able to receive on a real SSAT Middle Level test.

Good luck!

Time to Test

Time to refine your skill with a practice examination

Take a practice SSAT Middle Level Mathematics Test to simulate the test day experience. After you've finished, score your test using the answer keys.

Before You Start

- You'll need a pencil and a timer to take the test.

- After you've finished the test, review the answer key to see where you went wrong.

- Use the answer sheet provided to record your answers. (You can cut it out or photocopy it)

- You will receive 1 point for every correct answer, and you will lose $\frac{1}{4}$ point for each incorrect answer. There is no penalty for skipping a question.

Calculators are NOT permitted for the SSAT Middle Level Test

Good Luck!

SSAT Middle Level Math Practice Test 1

2020 - 2021

Two Parts

Total number of questions: 50

Section 1: 25 questions

Section 2: 25 questions

Total time for two parts: 60 Minutes

SSAT Middle Level Math Practice Test 1 Answer Sheet

Remove (or photocopy) this answer sheet and use it to complete the practice test.

SSAT Middle Level Mathematics Practice Test 1 Answer Sheet

SSAT Middle Level Practice Test 1 Section 1

#	Answer	#	Answer	#	Answer
1	A B C D E	11	A B C D E	21	A B C D E
2	A B C D E	12	A B C D E	22	A B C D E
3	A B C D E	13	A B C D E	23	A B C D E
4	A B C D E	14	A B C D E	24	A B C D E
5	A B C D E	15	A B C D E	25	A B C D E
6	A B C D E	16	A B C D E		
7	A B C D E	17	A B C D E		
8	A B C D E	18	A B C D E		
9	A B C D E	19	A B C D E		
10	A B C D E	20	A B C D E		

SSAT Middle Level Practice Test 1 Section 2

#	Answer	#	Answer	#	Answer
1	A B C D E	11	A B C D E	21	A B C D E
2	A B C D E	12	A B C D E	22	A B C D E
3	A B C D E	13	A B C D E	23	A B C D E
4	A B C D E	14	A B C D E	24	A B C D E
5	A B C D E	15	A B C D E	25	A B C D E
6	A B C D E	16	A B C D E		
7	A B C D E	17	A B C D E		
8	A B C D E	18	A B C D E		
9	A B C D E	19	A B C D E		
10	A B C D E	20	A B C D E		

SSAT Middle Level Math

Practice Test 1

Section 1

25 questions

Total time for this test: 30 Minutes

You may NOT use a calculator on this part.

1. How long does a 420–miles trip take moving at 65 miles per hour (mph)?
   (A) 4 $hours$
   (B) 6 $hours$ and 24 $minutes$
   (C) 8 $hours$ and 24 $minutes$
   (D) 8 $hours$ and 30 $minutes$
   (E) 10 $hours$ and 30 $minutes$

2. The marked price of a computer is D dollar. Its price decreased by 15% in January and later increased by 10% in February. What is the final price of the computer in D dollar?
   (A) 0.80 D
   (B) 0.88 D
   (C) 0.93 D
   (D) 1.20 D
   (E) 1.40 D

3. If 0.35 equals 350M, what is the value of M?
   (A) 0.001
   (B) 0.01
   (C) 1.0
   (D) 1.01
   (E) 1.001

4. Jason borrowed $5,800 for three months at an annual rate of 5%. How much interest did Jason owe?
   (A) $45
   (B) $72.50
   (C) $120
   (D) $240
   (E) $480

5. If three times a certain number, increased by 10, is equal to 40, what is the number?
   (A) 10
   (B) 12
   (C) 18
   (D) 27
   (E) 54

6. If 30 percent of a number is 150, then 15 percent of the same number is ?
   (A) 75
   (B) 79
   (C) 80
   (D) 90
   (E) 120

7. The average of $13, 15, 20$ and x is 20. What is the value of x?
   (A) 9
   (B) 15
   (C) 18
   (D) 20
   (E) 32

8. In five successive hours, a car traveled $40\ km, 45\ km, 50\ km, 35\ km$ and $55\ km$. In the next five hours, it traveled with an average speed of $55\ km\ per\ hour$. Find the total distance the car traveled in 10 hours.
   (A) $425\ km$
   (B) $450\ km$
   (C) $475\ km$
   (D) $500\ km$
   (E) $1,000\ km$

9. John has N toy cars. Jack has 6 more cars than John. If Jack gives John 3 cars, how many cars will Jack have, in terms of N?
   (A) N
   (B) $N - 1$
   (C) $N + 1$
   (D) $N + 2$
   (E) $N + 3$

10. What is the value of x in the following equation?

$$\frac{x + 4}{5} = 3$$

   (A) 2
   (B) 4
   (C) 6
   (D) 8
   (E) 11

11. The ratio of boys to girls in a school is $2 : 3$. If there are 500 students in a school, how many boys are in the school.
   (A) 540
   (B) 360
   (C) 300
   (D) 280
   (E) 200

12. Two third of 24 is equal to $\frac{2}{5}$ of what number?

    (A) 12

    (B) 20

    (C) 40

    (D) 60

    (E) 90

13. What is the cost of seven ounces of cheese at $0.96 *per pound*?

    (A) $0.42

    (B) $0.45

    (C) $0.48

    (D) $0.52

    (E) $0.64

14. If 60% of A is 30% of B, then B is what percent of A?

    (A) 3%

    (B) 30%

    (C) 200%

    (D) 300%

    (E) 900%

15. Sophia purchased a sofa for $504. The sofa is regularly priced at $600. What was the percent discount Sophia received on the sofa?

    (A) 12%

    (B) 16%

    (C) 20%

    (D) 25%

    (E) 40%

16. A bag contains 18 balls: two green, five black, eight blue, a brown, a red and one white. If 17 balls are removed from the bag at random, what is the probability that a brown ball has been removed?

    (A) $\frac{1}{9}$

    (B) $\frac{1}{18}$

    (C) $\frac{16}{17}$

    (D) $\frac{17}{18}$

    (E) $\frac{1}{2}$

17. When a number is subtracted from 28 and the difference is divided by that number, the result is 3. What is the value of the number?

   (A) 2
   (B) 4
   (C) 7
   (D) 12
   (E) 24

18. If 45% of a class are girls, and 25% of girls play tennis, approximately what percent of the class play tennis?

   (A) 11%
   (B) 15%
   (C) 20%
   (D) 40%
   (E) 80%

19. 44 students took an exam and 11 of them failed. What percent of the students passed the exam?

   (A) 20%
   (B) 40%
   (C) 60%
   (D) 75%
   (E) 90%

20. What is the value of x in the following equation?

$$3x + 10 = 67$$

   (A) 5
   (B) 7
   (C) 9
   (D) 11
   (E) 19

21. If $N \times \frac{4}{3} \times 7 = 0$, then $N =$....

   (A) 0
   (B) 1
   (C) 2
   (D) 3
   (E) 4

22. Jason left a $12.00 tip on a lunch that cost $60.00, approximately what percentage was the tip?

  (A) 2.5%
  (B) 10%
  (C) 15%
  (D) 20%
  (E) 25%

23. If 60% of a number is 6, what is the number?
  (A) 4
  (B) 8
  (C) 10
  (D) 12
  (E) 20

24. If $\frac{z}{5} = 4$, then $z + 3 =$?
  (A) 4
  (B) 5
  (C) 15
  (D) 20
  (E) 23

25. In 1999, the average worker's income increased $3,000 per year starting from $24,000 annual salary. Which equation represents income greater than average? ($I =$ income, x = number of years after 1999)
  (A) $I > 3,000x + 24,000$
  (B) $I > -3,000x + 24,000$
  (C) $I < -3,000x + 24,000$
  (D) $I < 3,000x - 24,000$
  (E) $I < 24,000x + 24,000$

SSAT Middle Level Math Workbook 2020 - 2021

SSAT Middle Level Math

Practice Test 1

Section 2

25 questions

Total time for this test: 30 Minutes

You may NOT use a calculator on this part.

1. John has x dollars and he receives $150. He then buys a bicycle that costs $110. How much money does John have now?
   (A) $x + 150$
   (B) $x + 110$
   (C) $x + 40$
   (D) $x - 120$
   (E) $x - 40$

2. What is the value of x in this equation?
$$\frac{x - 3}{8} + 5 = 20$$
   (A) 131
   (B) 128
   (C) 123
   (D) 120
   (E) 115

3. Bob needs an 78% average in his writing class to pass. On his first 4 exams, he earned scores of 68%, 72%, 85%, and 90%. What is the minimum score Bob can earn on his fifth and final test to pass?
   (A) 80%,
   (B) 75%
   (C) 68%
   (D) 64%
   (E) 60%

4. The width of a rectangle is $6x$, the length is $8x$, and the perimeter is 84. What is the value of x?
   (A) 1
   (B) 2
   (C) 3
   (D) 4
   (E) 5

5. A bank is offering 3.5% simple interest on a savings account. If you deposit $8,000, how much interest will you earn in five years?
   (A) $360
   (B) $720
   (C) $1,400
   (D) $3,600
   (E) $4,800

6. If $(8 - 4) \times 4 = 8 + \square$, then $\square = ?$
    (A) 5
    (B) 6
    (C) 7
    (D) 8
    (E) 9

7. Jason is 9 miles ahead of Joe running at 6.5 miles per hour and Joe is running at the speed of 8 miles per hour. How long does it take Joe to catch Jason?
    (A) 3 *hours*
    (B) 4 *hours*
    (C) 6 *hours*
    (D) 8 *hours*
    (E) 10 *hours*

8. In a classroom, there are y tables that can each seat 4 people and there are x tables that can each seat 8 people. What is the number of people that can be seated in the classroom?
    (A) $4y$
    (B) $8x$
    (C) $8x - 4y$
    (D) 13
    (E) $8x + 4y$

9. The area of a circle is 81π. What is the diameter of the circle?
    (A) 4
    (B) 8
    (C) 12
    (D) 14
    (E) 18

10. A shirt costing \$300 is discounted 15%. After a month, the shirt is discounted another 15%. Which of the following expressions can be used to find the selling price of the shirt?
    A. $(300)\,(0.70)$
    B. $(300) - 300\,(0.30)$
    C. $(300)(0.15) - (300)\,(0.15)$
    D. $(300)\,(0.85)\,(0.85)$
    E. $(300)(0.85)(0.85) - (300)\,(0.15)$

11. Four one – foot rulers can be split among how many users to leave each with $\frac{1}{3}$ of a ruler?
    (A) 4
    (B) 6
    (C) 12
    (D) 24
    (E) 48

12. The perimeter of a rectangular yard is 72 meters. What is its length if its width is twice its length?
   (A) 12 $meters$
   (B) 18 $meters$
   (C) 20 $meters$
   (D) 24 $meters$
   (E) 36 $meters$

13. What is the value of x in this equation? $2x + 10 = 48$
   (A) 19
   (B) 14
   (C) 12
   (D) 10
   (E) 6

14. The mean of 50 test scores was calculated as 86. But, it turned out that one of the scores was misread as 94 but it was 69. What is the mean?
   (A) 85.5
   (B) 85
   (C) 84.5
   (D) 83.5
   (E) 80.5

15. The average of 6 numbers is 15. The average of 4 of those numbers is 10. What is the average of the other two numbers?
   (A) 10
   (B) 12
   (C) 14
   (D) 15
   (E) 25

16. If $x + 5 = 8$, $2y - 1 = 5$ then $xy + 15 =$
   (A) 10
   (B) 19
   (C) 24
   (D) 27
   (E) 32

17. A card is drawn at random from a standard 52–card deck, what is the probability that the card is of Hearts? (The deck includes 13 of each suit clubs, diamonds, hearts, and spades)

(A) $\frac{1}{3}$

(B) $\frac{1}{4}$

(C) $\frac{1}{6}$

(D) $\frac{1}{52}$

(E) $\frac{1}{104}$

18. Which of the following is NOT less than $\frac{1}{5}$?

(A) $\frac{1}{8}$

(B) $\frac{1}{3}$

(C) $\frac{1}{9}$

(D) 0.14

(E) 17%

19. Mr. Jones saves $2,500 out of his monthly family income of $65,000. What fractional part of his income does he save?

(A) $\frac{1}{26}$

(B) $\frac{1}{11}$

(C) $\frac{3}{25}$

(D) $\frac{2}{15}$

(E) $\frac{1}{15}$

20. If $5x - 6 = 39$, then $3x + 6 =?$

(A) 18

(B) 20

(C) 22

(D) 33

(E) 36

21. In two successive years, the population of a town is increased by 10% and 20%. What percent of the population is increased after two years?

(A) 32%

(B) 31%

(C) 30%

(D) 28%

(E) 22%

22. If 150% of a number is 75, then what is the 80% of that number?

(A) 40
(B) 50
(C) 70
(D) 85
(E) 90

23. What is the equivalent temperature of $140°F$ in Celsius? ($C = Celsius$)
$$C = \frac{5}{9}(F - 32)$$

(A) 32
(B) 40
(C) 48
(D) 52
(E) 60

24. The perimeter of the trapezoid below is $50\ cm$. What is its area?

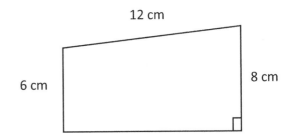

(A) $48\ cm^2$
(B) $70\ cm^2$
(C) $168\ cm^2$
(D) $576\ cm^2$
(E) $986\ cm^2$

25. The width of a box is one third of its length. The height of the box is half of its width. If the length of the box is $24\ cm$, what is the volume of the box?
(A) $81\ cm^3$
(B) $162\ cm^3$
(C) $243\ cm^3$
(D) $768\ \ cm^3$
(E) $1880\ \ cm^3$

IF YOU FINISH BEFORE TIME IS CALLED, YOU MAY CHECK YOUR WORK ON THIS SECTION ONLY. DO NOT TURN TO OTHER SECTION IN THE TEST. **STOP**

SSAT Middle Level Math Practice Test 2

2020 - 2021

Two Parts

Total number of questions: 50

Section 1: 25 questions

Section 2: 25 questions

Total time for two parts: 60 Minutes

SSAT Practice Test 2 Answer Sheet

Remove (or photocopy) this answer sheet and use it to complete the practice test.

SSAT Middle Level Mathematics Practice Test 2 Answer Sheet

SSAT Middle Level Practice Test 2 Section 1

1	(A) (B) (C) (D) (E)	11	(A) (B) (C) (D) (E)	21	(A) (B) (C) (D) (E)
2	(A) (B) (C) (D) (E)	12	(A) (B) (C) (D) (E)	22	(A) (B) (C) (D) (E)
3	(A) (B) (C) (D) (E)	13	(A) (B) (C) (D) (E)	23	(A) (B) (C) (D) (E)
4	(A) (B) (C) (D) (E)	14	(A) (B) (C) (D) (E)	24	(A) (B) (C) (D) (E)
5	(A) (B) (C) (D) (E)	15	(A) (B) (C) (D) (E)	25	(A) (B) (C) (D) (E)
6	(A) (B) (C) (D) (E)	16	(A) (B) (C) (D) (E)		
7	(A) (B) (C) (D) (E)	17	(A) (B) (C) (D) (E)		
8	(A) (B) (C) (D) (E)	18	(A) (B) (C) (D) (E)		
9	(A) (B) (C) (D) (E)	19	(A) (B) (C) (D) (E)		
10	(A) (B) (C) (D) (E)	20	(A) (B) (C) (D) (E)		

SSAT Middle Level Practice Test 2 Section 2

1	(A) (B) (C) (D) (E)	11	(A) (B) (C) (D) (E)	21	(A) (B) (C) (D) (E)
2	(A) (B) (C) (D) (E)	12	(A) (B) (C) (D) (E)	22	(A) (B) (C) (D) (E)
3	(A) (B) (C) (D) (E)	13	(A) (B) (C) (D) (E)	23	(A) (B) (C) (D) (E)
4	(A) (B) (C) (D) (E)	14	(A) (B) (C) (D) (E)	24	(A) (B) (C) (D) (E)
5	(A) (B) (C) (D) (E)	15	(A) (B) (C) (D) (E)	25	(A) (B) (C) (D) (E)
6	(A) (B) (C) (D) (E)	16	(A) (B) (C) (D) (E)		
7	(A) (B) (C) (D) (E)	17	(A) (B) (C) (D) (E)		
8	(A) (B) (C) (D) (E)	18	(A) (B) (C) (D) (E)		
9	(A) (B) (C) (D) (E)	19	(A) (B) (C) (D) (E)		
10	(A) (B) (C) (D) (E)	20	(A) (B) (C) (D) (E)		

SSAT Middle Level Math

Practice Test 2

Section 1

25 questions

Total time for this test: 30 Minutes

You may NOT use a calculator on this part.

1. If 15 percent of a number is 60, then 25 percent of the same number is ...
   (A) 65
   (B) 70
   (C) 80
   (D) 100
   (E) 120

2. Which of the following is NOT equal to 0.2×4?
   (A) 0.4×2
   (B) 1×0.8
   (C) $\frac{16}{8} \times \frac{4}{10}$
   (D) $\frac{5}{15} \times 3$
   (E) 0.8×1

3. Sara has N books. Mary has 5 more books than Sara. If Mary gives Sara 4 books, how many books will Mary have, in terms of N?
   (A) N
   (B) $N + 1$
   (C) $N + 2$
   (D) $N + 5$
   (E) $N - 5$

4. If $\frac{3x}{2} = 30$, then $\frac{2x}{5}$=?
   (A) 8
   (B) 10
   (C) 15
   (D) 20
   (E) 40

5. Which of the following is closest to $\frac{1}{5}$ of 40?
   (A) 0.3×6
   (B) 0.3×5
   (C) 0.2×30
   (D) 0.2×35
   (E) 0.2×39.5

6. What is the area of a square whose diagonal is 6?
   (A) 18
   (B) 24
   (C) 36
   (D) 60
   (E) 64

7. An angle is equal to one eighth of its supplement. What is the measure of that angle?
    A. 15
    B. 20
    C. 30
    D. 45
    E. 160

8. A $40 shirt now selling for $28 is discounted by what percent?
    (A) 20%
    (B) 30%
    (C) 40%
    (D) 60%
    (E) 80%

9. What is the value of x in the following figure? (Figure is not drawn to scale)
    (A) 150
    (B) 145
    (C) 125
    (D) 105
    (E) 85

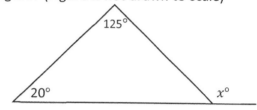

10. The perimeter of the trapezoid below is 54. What is its area?
    (A) $252cm^2$
    (B) $234\ cm^2$
    (C) $216\ cm^2$
    (D) $130\ cm^2$
    (E) $108\ cm^2$

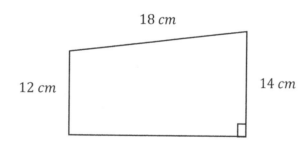

11. The score of Emma was half as that of Ava and the score of Mia was twice that of Ava. If the score of Mia was 60, what is the score of Emma?
    (A) 15
    (B) 18
    (C) 20
    (D) 30
    (E) 32

12. Two third of 30 is equal to $\frac{2}{5}$ of what number?
   (A) 15
   (B) 20
   (C) 30
   (D) 50
   (E) 60

13. If three times a number added to 6 equals to 30, what is the number?
   (A) 2
   (B) 4
   (C) 6
   (D) 8
   (E) 10

14. Solve for x: $4(x + 2) = 6(x - 4) + 20$
   (A) 12
   (B) 6
   (C) 5.5
   (D) 4
   (E) 2

15. Five years ago, Amy was three times as old as Mike was. If Mike is 10 years old now, how old is Amy?

   (A) 4
   (B) 8
   (C) 12
   (D) 15
   (E) 20

16. Two-kilograms apple and three-kilograms orange cost $26.4. If one-kilogram apple costs $4.2 how much does one-kilogram orange cost?
   (A) $9
   (B) $6
   (C) $5.5
   (D) $5
   (E) $4.5

17. The average weight of 18 girls in a class is $60 \, kg$ and the average weight of 32 boys in the same class is $62 \, kg$. What is the average weight of all the 50 students in that class?
   A. 61.28
   B. 61.68
   C. 61.90
   D. 62.20
   E. 64.00

18. What is the value of x in this equation? $6(x + 4) = 72$
    (A) 4
    (B) 6
    (C) 8
    (D) 10
    (E) 12

19. When a number is subtracted from 20 and the difference is divided by that number, the result is 3. What is the value of the number?

    (A) 2

    (B) 4

    (C) 5

    (D) 12

    (E) 15

20. Which of the following is the correct statement?
    (A) $\frac{3}{4} > 0.8$
    (B) $10\% = \frac{2}{5}$
    (C) $3 < \frac{5}{2}$
    (D) $\frac{5}{6} > 0.8$
    (E) $2.5\% = 0.25$

21. In a group of 5 books, the average number of pages is 24. Mary adds a book with 30 pages to the group. What is the new average number of pages per book?
    (A) 20
    (B) 22
    (C) 24
    (D) 25
    (E) 30

22. A football team won exactly 80% of the games it played during last session. Which of the following could be the total number of games the team played last season?
    (A) 49
    (B) 35
    (C) 32
    (D) 12
    (E) 8

23. If a gas tank can hold 25 gallons, how many gallons does it contain when it is $\frac{2}{5}$ full?
    (A) 50
    (B) 125
    (C) 62.5
    (D) 10
    (E) 8

24. A red box is 20% greater than a blue box. If 30 books exist in the red box, how many books are in the blue box?

    (A) 9

    (B) 15

    (C) 20

    (D) 25

    (E) 26

25. 6 liters of water are poured into an aquarium that's 15 cm long, 5 cm wide, and 90 cm high. How many cm will the water level in the aquarium rise due to this added water? (1 $liter\ of\ water = 1,000\ cm^3$)
    A. 80
    B. 40
    C. 20
    D. 10
    E. 8

IF YOU FINISH BEFORE TIME IS CALLED, YOU MAY CHECK YOUR WORK ON THIS SECTION ONLY. DO NOT TURN TO OTHER SECTION IN THE TEST. STOP

116   SSAT Middle Level Math Workbook 2020 - 2021

SSAT Middle Level Mathematics

Practice Test 2

Section 2

25 questions

Total time for this test: 30 Minutes

You may NOT use a calculator for this test.

1. A taxi driver earns $9 per 1-hour work. If he works 10 hours a day and in 1 hour he uses 2-liters petrol with price $1 for 1-liter. How much money does he earn in one day?
    (A) $90
    (B) $88
    (C) $70
    (D) $60
    (E) $56

2. Which of the following is less than $\frac{1}{5}$?
    (A) $\frac{1}{4}$
    (B) 0.5
    (C) $\frac{1}{6}$
    (D) 0.25
    (E) 0.3

3. Amy and John work in a same company. Last month, both of them received a raise of 20 percent. If Amy earns $30.00 *per hour* now and John earns $26.40, Amy earned how much more per hour than John before their raises?
    (A) $8.25
    (B) $4.25
    (C) $3.00
    (D) $2.25
    (E) $1.75

4. Four people can paint 4 houses in 10 days. How many people are needed to paint 8 houses in 5 days?
    (A) 6
    (B) 8
    (C) 12
    (D) 16
    (E) 20

5. If $N \times (5 - 3) = 12$ then $N =$?
    (A) 6
    (B) 12
    (C) 13
    (D) 14
    (E) 18

6. The length of a rectangle is 3 times of its width. If the length is 18, what is the perimeter of the rectangle?
   (A) 24
   (B) 30
   (C) 36
   (D) 48
   (E) 56

7. In the figure below, what is the value of x? (Figure is not drawn to scale)
   (A) 43
   (B) 67
   (C) 77
   (D) 90
   (E) 98

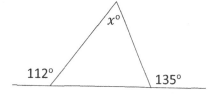

8. If $x \blacksquare y = 3x + y - 2$, what is the value of $4 \blacksquare 12$?
   (A) 4
   (B) 18
   (C) 22
   (D) 36
   (E) 48

9. The width of a rectangle is $4x$. the length is $6x$, and the perimeter of the rectangle is 80. What is the value of x?
   (A) 1
   (B) 2
   (C) 3
   (D) 4
   (E) 5

10. How many tiles of $8\ cm^2$ is needed to cover a floor of dimension $6\ cm$ by $24\ cm$?
   (A) 6
   (B) 12
   (C) 18
   (D) 24
   (E) 30

11. If 0.45 equals $450M$, what is the value of M?
   (A) 0.0001
   (B) 0.001
   (C) 0.01
   (D) 1.00
   (E) 0.11

12. If $z = 3x + 6$, what does $2z + 3$ equal?

(A) $6x + 6$

(B) $6x + 12$

(C) $6x - 12$

(D) $6x - 6$

(E) $6x + 15$

13. If 20 is the product of 2 and $2x$, then 20 is divisible by which of the following?

(A) $x + 4$

(B) $2x - 4$

(C) $x - 2$

(D) $x \times 4$

(E) $x + 1$

$$0.\,ABC \qquad\qquad 0.0D$$

14. The letters represent two decimals listed above. One of the decimals is equivalent to $\frac{1}{8}$ and the other is equivalent to $\frac{1}{20}$. What is the product of C and D?

(A) 0

(B) 5

(C) 25

(D) 20

(E) 40

15. $\dfrac{x}{x-3} = \dfrac{4}{5}$, $x - 5 =?$

(A) -12

(B) -15

(C) -17

(D) 12

(E) 15

16. A company pays its employee $4,000 plus 2% of all sales profit. If x is the number of all sales profit, which of the following represents the employer's revenue?

(A) $0.02x$

(B) $0.98x - 4,000$

(C) $0.02x + 4,000$

(D) $0.98x + 4,000$

(E) $0.2x + 4,000$

17. In a certain bookshelf of a library, there are 35 biology books, 95 history books, and 80 language books. What is the ratio of the number of biology books to the total number of books in this bookshelf?

(A) $\frac{1}{4}$

(B) $\frac{1}{6}$

(C) $\frac{2}{7}$

(D) $\frac{3}{8}$

(E) $\frac{1}{4}$

18. If $6,000 + A - 200 = 7,400$, then $A = \cdots$
   (A) 200
   (B) 600
   (C) 1,600
   (D) 2,200
   (E) 3,000

19. The circle graph below shows all Mr. Taylor's expenses for last month. If he spent $660 on his car, how much did he spend for his rent?

(A) $700
(B) $740
(C) $780
(D) $810
(E) $900

Mr. Green's monthly expenses

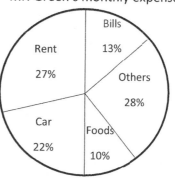

20. If $5 \times M + 4 = 5$, M equals to ….
   (A) 2
   (B) 4
   (C) $\frac{1}{5}$
   (D) 6
   (E) $\frac{1}{3}$

21. Which of the following is equal to $\frac{42.6}{100}$?
   (A) 42.6
   (B) 4.26
   (C) 426.0
   (D) 0.0426
   (E) 0.426

22. In the following figure, point Q lies on line n, what is the value of y if $x = 35$? (Figure is not drawn to scale)
    (A) 15
    (B) 25
    (C) 35
    (D) 45
    (E) 60

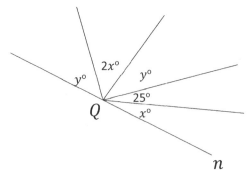

23. A container holds 3.5 gallons of water when it is $\frac{7}{24}$ full. How many gallons of water does the container hold when it's full?
    (A) 8
    (B) 12
    (C) 16
    (D) 20
    (E) 30

24. At a Zoo, the ratio of lions to tigers is 5 to 3. Which of the following could NOT be the total number of lions and tigers in the zoo?
    (A) 64
    (B) 80
    (C) 98
    (D) 104
    (E) 160

25. If x is greater than 48, then $\frac{1}{6}$ of x must be...
    (A) Greater than 12
    (B) Greater than 16
    (C) Equal to 16
    (D) Equal to 12
    (E) Less than 12

IF YOU FINISH BEFORE TIME IS CALLED, YOU MAY CHECK YOUR WORK ON THIS SECTION ONLY. DO NOT TURN TO ANY OTHER SECTION IN THE TEST. STOP

122   SSAT Middle Level Math Workbook 2020 - 2021

SSAT Middle Level Math Practice Test Answers and Explanations

Now, it's time to review your results to see where you went wrong and what areas you need to improve

SSAT Middle Level Math Practice Test 1								SSAT Middle Level Math Practice Test 2							
Section 1				Section 2				Section 1				Section 2			
1	B	16	D	1	C	16	C	1	D	16	B	1	C	16	C
2	C	17	C	2	C	17	B	2	D	17	A	2	C	17	B
3	A	18	A	3	B	18	B	3	B	18	C	3	C	18	C
4	B	19	D	4	C	19	A	4	A	19	C	4	D	19	D
5	A	20	E	5	C	20	D	5	E	20	D	5	A	20	C
6	A	21	A	6	D	21	A	6	A	21	D	6	D	21	E
7	E	22	D	7	C	22	A	7	B	22	B	7	B	22	B
8	D	23	C	8	E	23	E	8	B	23	D	8	C	23	B
9	E	24	E	9	E	24	C	9	B	24	D	9	D	24	C
10	E	25	A	10	D	25	D	10	D	25	A	10	C	25	A
11	E			11	C			11	A			11	B		
12	C			12	A			12	D			12	E		
13	A			13	A			13	D			13	D		
14	C			14	A			14	B			14	C		
15	B			15	E			15	E			15	C		

Score Your Test

SSAT scores are broken down by its three sections: Verbal, Mathematics, and Reading. A sum of the three sections is also reported.

For the Middle Level SSAT, the score range is 500-800, the lowest possible score a student can earn is 500 and the highest score is 800 for each section. A student receives 1 point for every correct answer and loses $\frac{1}{4}$ point for each incorrect answer. No points are lost by skipping a question.

The total scaled score for a Middle Level SSAT test is the sum of the scores for the Mathematics, verbal, and reading sections. A student will also receive a percentile score of between 1-99% that compares that student's test scores with those of other test takers of same grade and gender from the past 3 years.

Use the following table to convert SSAT Middle level raw score to scaled score.

SSAT Middle Level Math Scaled Scores	
Raw Scores	Mathematics
50	710
45	680
40	660
35	635
30	615
25	590
20	570
15	540
10	525
5	500
0	480
-5	460
- 10 and lower	440

SSAT Middle Level Mathematics Practice Test 1 Section 1

1) Choice B is correct

Use distance formula: $Distance = Rate \times time \Rightarrow 420 = 65 \times T$, divide both sides by 65. $420 \div 65 = T \Rightarrow T = 6.4\ hours$. Change hours to minutes for the decimal part.

$$0.4\ hours = 0.4 \times 60 = 24\ minutes.$$

2) Choice C is correct

To find the discount, multiply the number by $(100\% - rate\ of\ discount)$.Therefore, for the first discount we get: $(D)(100\% - 15\%) = (D)(0.85) = 0.85\ D$

For increase of 10%: $(0.85\ D)(100\% + 10\%) = (0.85\ D)(1.10) = 0.93\ D = 93\%\ of\ D\ or\ 0.93D$

3) Choice A is correct

0.35 equals $350M$. Then:$0.35 = 350M \rightarrow M = \frac{0.35}{350} = 0.001$

4) Choice B is correct

Use simple interest formula:$I = prt$, (I = interest, p = principal, r = rate, t = time)

t is for one year. For 3 months, t is $\frac{1}{4}$ or 0.25. $I = (5,800)(0.05)(0.25) = 72.50$

5) Choice A is correct

Three times a certain number, increased by 10, is equal to 40. Write an equation and solve.

$$3x + 10 = 40 \rightarrow 3x = 40 - 10 = 30 \rightarrow x = \frac{30}{3} = 10$$

6) Choice A is correct

30 percent of a number is 150. Therefore, the number is 500. $0.30x = 150 \rightarrow x = \frac{150}{0.30} = 500$

15 percent of 500 is 75. $0.15 \times 500 = 75$

7) Choice E is correct

$$average = \frac{sum\ of\ terms}{number\ of\ terms} \Rightarrow 20 = \frac{13 + 15 + 20 + x}{4} \Rightarrow 80 = 48 + x \Rightarrow x = 32$$

8) Choice D is correct

Add the first 5 numbers. $40 + 45 + 50 + 35 + 55 = 225$

To find the distance traveled in the next 5 hours, multiply the average by number of hours.

$Distance = Average \times Rate = 55 \times 5 = 275$, Add both numbers. $275 + 225 = 500$

9) Choice E is correct

John has N toy cars. Jack has 6 more cars than John. Therefore, Jack has $N + 6$ toy cars. Jack gives John 3 cars. Now, Jack has $(N + 6 - 3)$ $N + 3$ toy cars.

10) Choice E is correct

$$\frac{x + 4}{5} = 3 \rightarrow x + 4 = 3 \times 5 = 15 \rightarrow x = 15 - 4 = 11$$

11) Choice E is correct

Th ratio of boy to girls is $2 : 3$. Therefore, there are 2 boys out of 5 students. To find the answer, first divide the total number of students by 5, then multiply the result by 2.

$$500 \div 5 = 100 \Rightarrow 100 \times 2 = 200$$

12) Choice C is correct

Let x be the number. Write the equation and solve for x. $\frac{2}{3} \times 24 = \frac{2}{5} . x \Rightarrow \frac{2 \times 24}{3} = \frac{2x}{5}$, use cross multiplication to solve for x. $5 \times 48 = 2x \times 3 \Rightarrow 240 = 6x \Rightarrow x = 40$

13) Choice A is correct

One pound of cheese costs 0.96. *One pound* $= 16$ *ounces*, 16 ounces of cheese costs 0.96. Then, 1 ounce of chees costs $(0.96 \div 16)$ 0.06. 7 ounces of cheese costs $(7 \times \$0.06)$ 0.42.

14) Choice C is correct

Write the equation and solve for B: $0.60A = 0.30B$, divide both sides by 0.30, then you will have $\frac{0.60}{0.30}A = B$, therefore: $B = 2A$, and B is 2 times of A or it's 200% of A.

15) Choice B is correct

$\frac{504}{600} = 0.84$. 504 is 84 percent of 600. So, the discount is 16%. $100\% - 16\% = 84\%$

16) Choice D is correct

If 17 balls are removed from the bag at random, there will be one ball in the bag. The probability of choosing a brown ball is 1 out of 18. Therefore, the probability of not choosing a brown ball is 17 out of 18 and the probability of having not a brown ball after removing 17 balls is the same.

17) Choice C is correct

Let x be the number. Write the equation and solve for x. $(28 - x) \div x = 3$. Multiply both sides by x. $(28 - x) = 3x$, then add x both sides. $28 = 4x$, now divide both sides by 4. $x = 7$

18) Choice A is correct

The percent of girls playing tennis is: $45\% \times 25\% = 0.45 \times 0.25 \approx 0.11 = 11\%$

19) Choice D is correct

The failing rate is 11 out of $44 = \frac{11}{55}$. Change the fraction to percent: $\frac{11}{44} \times 100\% = 25\%$

25 percent of students failed. Therefore, 75 percent of students passed the exam.

20) Choice E is correct

$3x + 10 = 67 \rightarrow 3x = 67 - 10 = 57 \rightarrow x = \frac{57}{3} = 19$

21) Choice A is correct

$N \times \frac{4}{3} \times 7 = 0$, then N must be 0.

22) Choice D is correct

$12 **is what percent of** \$60? 12 \div 60 = 0.20 = 20\%$

23) Choice C is correct

Let x be the number. Write the equation and solve for x.

$60\% \; of \; x = 6 \Rightarrow 0.60 \, x = 6 \Rightarrow x = 6 \div 0.60 = 10$

24) Choice E is correct

$\frac{z}{5} = 4 \rightarrow z = 4 \times 5 = 20, z + 3 = 20 + 3 = 23$

25) Choice A is correct

Let x be the number of years. Therefore, \$3,000 per year equals $3000x$. starting from \$24,000 annual salary means you should add that amount to $2000x$. Income more than that is:

$I > 3000x + 24000$

SSAT Middle Level Mathematics Practice Test 1 Section 2

1) Choice C is correct

John has x dollars and he receives \$150. Therefore, he has $x + 150$.

He then buys a bicycle that costs \$110. Now, he has: $x + 150 - 110 = x + 40$

2) Choice C is correct

$\frac{x-3}{8} + 5 = 20 \rightarrow \frac{x-3}{8} = 20 - 5 = 15 \rightarrow x - 3 = 15 \times 8 = 120 \rightarrow$

$x = 120 + 3 = 123$

3) Choice B is correct

Bob needs an 78% average to pass for five exams. Therefore, the sum of 5 exams must be at lease $5 \times 78 = 390$, The sum of 4 exams is: $68 + 72 + 85 + 90 = 315$.

The minimum score Bob can earn on his fifth and final test to pass is: $390 - 315 = 75$

4) Choice C is correct

The width of a rectangle is $6x$ and its length is $8x$. Then, the perimeter of the rectangle is $28x$.

$Perimeter\ of\ a\ rectangle = 2(width + length) = 2(6x + 8x) = 28x$

The perimeter of the rectangle is 84. Then: $28x = 84 \rightarrow x = 3$

5) Choice C is correct

Use simple interest formula: $I = prt$, (I = interest, p = principal, r = rate, t = time)

$I = (8,000)(0.035)(5) = 1,400$

6) Choice D is correct

$(8 - 4) \times 4 = 8 + \square$

Then: $4 \times 4 = 8 + \square$, $16 = 8 + \square$, then $\square = 8$

7) Choice C is correct

The distance between Jason and Joe is 9 miles. Jason running at 6.5 miles per hour and Joe is running at the speed of 8 miles per hour. Therefore, every hour the distance is 1.5 miles less.

$9 \div 1.5 = 6$

8) Choice E is correct

There are y tables that can each seat 4 people and there are x tables that can each seat 8 people. Therefore, $4y + 8x$ people can be seated in the classroom

9) Choice E is correct

The formula for the area of the circle is: $A = \pi r^2$

The area of the circle is 81π. **Therefore:** $A = \pi r^2 \Rightarrow 81\pi = \pi r^2$, **Divide both sides by** π: $81 = r^2 \Rightarrow r = 9$, Diameter of a circle is $2 \times$ radius. Then: Diameter $= 2 \times 9 = 18$

10) Choice D is correct

To find the discount, multiply the number by $(100\% - rate\ of\ discount)$. Therefore, for the first discount we get: $(300)\ (100\% - 15\%) = (300)\ (0.85)$, For the next 15% discount: $(300)\ (0.85)\ (0.85)$

11) Choice C is correct

$4 \div \dfrac{1}{3} = 12$

12) Choice A is correct

The width of the rectangle is twice its length. Let x be the length. Then, $width = 2x$

Perimeter of the rectangle is 2 ($width + length$) $= 2(2x + x) = 72 \Rightarrow 6x = 72 \Rightarrow x = 12$

Length of the rectangle is 12 meters.

13) Choice A is correct

$2x + 10 = 48 \rightarrow 2x = 48 - 10 = 38 \rightarrow x = \dfrac{38}{2} = 19$

14) Choice A is correct

$$average \ (mean) = \frac{sum \ of \ terms}{number \ of \ terms} \Rightarrow 86 = \frac{sum \ of \ terms}{50} \Rightarrow sum = 86 \times 50$$
$$= 4300$$

The difference of 94 and 69 is 25. Therefore, 25 should be subtracted from the sum.

$4300 - 25 = 4275, mean = \dfrac{sum \ of \ terms}{number \ of \ terms} \Rightarrow mean = \dfrac{4275}{50} = 85.5$

15) Choice E is correct

$average = \dfrac{sum \ of \ terms}{number \ of \ terms} \Rightarrow$ (average of 6 numbers) $15 = \dfrac{sum \ of \ numbers}{6} \Rightarrow$ sum of 6 numbers is $15 \times 6 = 90$

(average of 4 numbers) $10 = \dfrac{sum \ of \ numbers}{4} \Rightarrow$ sum of 4 numbers is $10 \times 4 = 40$

$sum \ of \ 6 \ numbers - sum \ of \ 4 \ numbers = sum \ of \ 2 \ numbers$

$90 - 40 = 50$ average of 2 numbers $= \dfrac{50}{2} = 25$

16) Choice C is correct

$x + 5 = 8 \rightarrow x = 8 - 5 = 3, 2y - 1 = 5 \rightarrow 2y = 6 \rightarrow y = 3, xy + 15 = 3 \times 3 + 15 = 24$

17) Choice B is correct

The probability of choosing a Hearts is $\dfrac{13}{52} = \dfrac{1}{4}$

18) Choice B is correct

From the choices provided, only $\dfrac{1}{3}$ **is greater than** $\dfrac{1}{5}$**.**

19) Choice A is correct

2,500 out of 65,000 equals to $\dfrac{2500}{65000} = \dfrac{25}{650} = \dfrac{1}{26}$

20) Choice D is correct

$5x - 6 = 39 \rightarrow 5x = 39 + 6 = 45 \rightarrow x = 9$, then $3x + 6 = 3 \times 9 + 6 = 27 + 6 = 33$

21) Choice A is correct

the population is increased by 10% and 20%. 10% increase changes the population to 110% of original population. For the second increase, multiply the result by 120%.

SSAT Middle Level Math Workbook 2020 - 2021

$(1.10) \times (1.20) = 1.32 = 132\%$, 32 percent of the population is increased after two years.

22) Choice A is correct

First, find the number. Let x be the number. Write the equation and solve for x.

150% of a number is 75, then: $1.5 \times x = 75 \Rightarrow x = 75 \div 1.5 = 50$. 80% of 50 is: $0.8 \times 50 = 40$

23) Choice E is correct

Plug in 104 for F and then solve for C.

$$C = \frac{5}{9}(F - 32) \Rightarrow C = \frac{5}{9}(140 - 32) \Rightarrow C = \frac{5}{9}(108) = 60$$

24) Choice C is correct

The perimeter of the trapezoid is 50.

Therefore, the missing side (height) is $= 50 - 8 - 12 - 6 = 24$

Area of a trapezoid: $A = \frac{1}{2}h(b_1 + b_2) = \frac{1}{2}(24)(6 + 8) = 168$

25) Choice D is correct

If the length of the box is 24, then the width of the box is one third of it, 8, and the height of the box is 4 (half of the width). The volume of the box is:

$Volume\ of\ a\ box = (length) \times (width) \times (height) = (24) \times (8) \times (4) = 768$

SSAT Middle Level Mathematics Practice Test 2 Section 1

1) Choice D is correct

If 15 percent of a number is 60, then the number is: $15\%\ of\ x = 60 \rightarrow 0.15x = 60 \rightarrow x = \frac{60}{0.15} = 400$, 25 percent of 400 is: $25\%\ of\ 200 = \frac{25}{100} \times 400 = 100$

2) Choice D is correct

$0.2 \times 4 = 0.8$, all **choices** provided are equal to 0.8 except choice D. $\frac{5}{15} \times 3 = 1$

3) Choice B is correct

Sara has N books. Mary has 5 more books than Sara. Then, Mary has $N + 5$ books. If Mary gives Sara 4 books, Mary will have: $N + 5 - 4 = N + 1$

4) Choice A is correct

If $\frac{3x}{2} = 30$, then $3x = 60 \rightarrow x = 20$, $\frac{2x}{5} = \frac{2 \times 20}{5} = \frac{40}{5} = 8$

5) Choice E is correct

$\frac{1}{5}$ of 40 is 8. Let's review the **choices** provided:

(A) $0.3 \times 6 = 1.8$
(B) $0.3 \times 5 = 1.5$
(C) $0.2 \times 30 = 6$
(D) $0.2 \times 35 = 7$
(E) $0.2 \times 39.5 = 7.9$

Option E is the closest to 8.

6) Choice A is correct

The diagonal of the square is 6. Let x be the side.

Use Pythagorean Theorem: $a^2 + b^2 = c^2$

$x^2 + x^2 = 6^2 \Rightarrow 2x^2 = 6^2 \Rightarrow 2x^2 = 36 \Rightarrow x^2 = 18 \Rightarrow x = \sqrt{18}$

The area of the square is: $\sqrt{18} \times \sqrt{18} = 18$

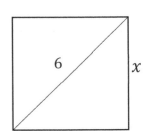

7) Choice B is correct

The sum of supplement angles is 180. Let x be that angle. Therefore, $x + 8x = 180$

$9x = 180$, divide both sides by 9: $x = 20$

8) Choice B is correct

Use the formula for Percent of Change: $\dfrac{\text{New Value} - \text{Old Value}}{Old\ Value} \times 100\%$

$\dfrac{28-40}{40} \times 100\% = -30\%$ (negative sign here means that the new price is less than old price)

9) Choice B is correct

$x = 20 + 125 = 145$

10) Choice D is correct

The perimeter of the trapezoid is 54.

Therefore, the missing side (height) is $= 54 - 18 - 12 - 14 = 10$

Area of the trapezoid: $A = \frac{1}{2} h (b_1 + b_2) = \frac{1}{2} (10) (12 + 14) = 130$

11) Choice A is correct

If the score of Mia was 60, therefore the score of Ava is 30. Since, the score of Emma was half as that of Ava, therefore, the score of Emma is 15.

12) Choice D is correct

Let x be the number. Write the equation and solve for x.

$\frac{2}{3} \times 30 = \frac{2}{5} \times x \Rightarrow \frac{2 \times 30}{3} = \frac{2x}{5}$, use cross multiplication to solve for x.

$5 \times 60 = 2x \times 3 \Rightarrow 300 = 6x \Rightarrow x = 50$

13) Choice D is correct

Let x be the number. Then: $3x + 6 = 30$, Solve for x: $3x + 6 = 30 \rightarrow 3x = 30 - 6 = 24 \rightarrow x = 24 \div 3 = 8$

14) Choice B is correct

Simplify and solve for x in the equation. $4(x + 2) = 6(x - 4) + 20 \rightarrow 4x + 8 = 6x - 24 + 20$

$4x + 8 = 6x - 4$, Subtract $4x$ from both sides: $8 = 2x - 4$, Add 4 to both sides: $12 = 2x, 6 = x$

15) Choice E is correct

Five years ago, Amy was three times as old as Mike. Mike is 10 years now. Therefore, 5 years ago Mike was 5 years. Five years ago, Amy was: $A = 3 \times 5 = 15$

Now Amy is 20 years old: $15 + 5 = 20$

16) Choice B is correct

Let x be one-kilogram orange cost, then: $3x + (2 \times 4.2) = 26.4 \rightarrow 3x + 8.4 = 26.4 \rightarrow$ $3x = 26.4 - 8.4 \rightarrow 3x = 18 \rightarrow x = \frac{18}{3} = \$6$

17) Choice A is correct

$average = \frac{sum\ of\ terms}{number\ of\ terms}$, The sum of the weight of all girls is: $18 \times 60 = 1080\ kg$, The sum of the weight of all boys is: $32 \times 62 = 1984\ kg$, The sum of the weight of all students is: $1,080 + 1,984 = 3,064\ kg$, $Average = \frac{3064}{50} = 61.28$

18) Choice C is correct

Solve for x in the equation. $6(x + 4) = 72 \rightarrow 6x + 24 = 72 \rightarrow 6x = 72 - 24 = 48 \rightarrow x = 48 \div 6 = 8$

19) Choice C is correct

Let x be the number. Write the equation and solve for x. $(20 - x) \div x = 3$
Multiply both sides by x. $(20 - x) = 3x$, then add x both sides. $20 = 4x$, now divide both sides by 4. $x = 5$

20) Choice D is correct

Only option D is correct. $\frac{5}{6} = 0.83 \rightarrow 0.8 < \frac{5}{6}$

21) Choice D is correct

In a group of 5 books, the average number of pages is 24. Therefore, the sum of pages in all 5 books is ($5 \times 24 = 120$). Mary adds a book with 30 pages to the group. Then, the sum of pages in all 6 books is ($5 \times 24 + 30 = 150$). The new average number of pages per book is: $\frac{150}{6} = 25$

22) Choice B is correct

Choices A, C, D, and E are incorrect because 80% of each of the numbers is a non-whole number.

A.	49	$80\% \ of \ 49 = 0.80 \times 49 = 39.2$
B.	35	$80\% \ of \ 35 = 0.80 \times 35 = 28$
C.	32	$80\% \ of \ 32 = 0.80 \times 32 = 25.6$
D.	12	$80\% \ of \ 12 = 0.80 \times 12 = 9.6$
E.	8	$80\% \ of \ 8 = 0.80 \times 8 = 6.4$

23) Choice D is correct

$$\frac{2}{5} \times 25 = \frac{50}{5} = 10$$

24) Choice D is correct

The red box is 20% greater than the blue box. Let x be the capacity of the blue box. Then:

$$x + 20\% \ of \ x = 30 \rightarrow 1.2x = 30 \rightarrow x = \frac{30}{1.2} = 25$$

25) Choice A is correct

$One \ liter = 1,000 \ cm^3 \rightarrow 6 \ liters = 6,000 \ cm^3$. Let's put h for the height of the water. Then:

$$6,000 = 15 \times 5 \times h \rightarrow h = \frac{6,000}{75} = 80 \ cm$$

SSAT Middle Level Mathematics Practice Test 2 Section 2

1) Choice C is correct

$\$9 \times 10 = \$90$, Petrol use: $10 \times 2 = 20$ liters, Petrol cost: $20 \times \$1 = \$20$

Money earned: $\$90 - \$20 = \$70$

2) Choice C is correct

From the **choices** provided, only C ($\frac{1}{6}$) is less than $\frac{1}{5}$.

3) Choice C is correct

Amy earns $\$30.00 \ per \ hour$ now. $\$30.00 \ per \ hour$ is 20 percent more than her previous rate. Let x be her rate before her raise. Then: $x + 0.20x = 30 \rightarrow 1.2x = 30 \rightarrow x = \frac{30}{1.2} = 25$

John earns $26.40 *per hour* now. $26.40 *per hour* is 20 percent more than his previous rate. Let x be John's rate before his raise. Then: $x + 0.20x = 26.40 \rightarrow 1.2x = 26.40 \rightarrow x = \frac{26.40}{1.2} = 22$, Amy earned $3.00 more per hour than John before their raises.

4) Choice D is correct.

Four people can paint 4 houses in 10 days. It means that for painting 8 houses in 10 days we need 8 people. To paint 8 houses in 5 days, 16 people are needed.

5) Choice A is correct.
$N \times (5 - 3) = 12 \rightarrow N \times 2 = 12 \rightarrow N = 6$

6) Choice D is correct.

The length of the rectangle is 18. Then, its width is 6. $18 \div 3 = 6$

$Perimeter\ of\ a\ rectangle = 2 \times width + 2 \times length = 2 \times 6 + 2 \times 18 = 12 + 36 = 48$

7) Choice B is correct

$\alpha = 180° - 112° = 68°$, $b = 180° - 135° = 45°$, The sum of all angles in a triangle is 180 degrees. Then:$x + \alpha + b = 180° \rightarrow x = 180° - 68° - 45° = 67°$

8) Choice C is correct.

If $x \blacksquare y = 3x + y - 2$, Then: $4 \blacksquare 12 = 3(4) + 12 - 2 = 12 + 12 - 2 = 22$

9) Choice D is correct

The width of a rectangle is $4x$ and its length is $6x$. Therefore, the perimeter of the rectangle is $20x$. $Perimeter\ of\ a\ rectangle = 2(width + length) = 2(4x + 6x) = 2(10x) = 20x$

The perimeter of the rectangle is 80. Then: $20x = 80 \rightarrow x = 4$

10) Choice C is correct

The area of the floor is: $6\ cm \times 24\ cm = 144\ cm^2$, The number is tiles needed $= 144 \div 8 = 18$

11) Choice B is correct

0.45 equals $450M$. Then: $450M = 0.45 \rightarrow M = \frac{0.45}{450} = 0.001$

12) Choice E is correct

$z = 3x + 6$, then, $2z = 2(3x + 6) = 6x + 12$, $2z + 3 = 6x + 12 + 3 = 6x + 15$

13) Choice D is correct.

$20 = 2x \times 2 \rightarrow x = 20 \div 4 = 5$
x equals to 5. Let's review the **choices** provided:

A) $x + 4 \rightarrow 5 + 4 = 9$ 20 is not divisible by 9.
B) $2x - 4 \rightarrow 2 \times 5 - 4 = 6$ 20 is not divisible by 6.
C) $x - 2 \rightarrow 5 - 2 = 3$ 20 is not divisible by 3.
D) $x \times 4 \rightarrow 5 \times 4 = 20$ 20 is divisible by 20.
E) $x + 1 \rightarrow 5 + 1 = 6$ 20 is not divisible by 6.

The answer is D.

14) Choice C is correct

$\frac{1}{8} = 0.125 \rightarrow C = 5,$ $\frac{1}{20} = 0.05 \rightarrow D = 5 \rightarrow C \times D = 5 \times 5 = 25$

15) Choice C is correct

Use cross product to solve for x. $\frac{x}{x-3} = \frac{4}{5} \rightarrow 5 \times x = 4 \times (x - 3) \rightarrow 5x = 4x - 12 \rightarrow x = -12$

$\rightarrow x - 5 = -12 - 5 = -17$

16) Choice C is correct

x is the number of all sales profit and 2% of it is: $2\% \times x = 0.02x$, Employee's revenue:

$$0.02x + 4{,}000$$

17) Choice B is correct

Number of biology book: 35, total number of books; $35 + 95 + 80 = 210$

the ratio of the number of biology books to the total number of books is: $\frac{35}{210} = \frac{1}{6}$

18) Choice C is correct.

$6{,}000 + A - 200 = 7{,}400 \rightarrow 6{,}000 + A = 7{,}400 + 200 = 7{,}600 \rightarrow A = 7{,}600 - 6{,}000 = 1{,}600$

19) Choice D is correct

Let x be all expenses, then $\frac{22}{100}x = \$660 \rightarrow x = \frac{100 \times \$660}{22} = \$3{,}000$

Mr. Jones spent for his rent: $\frac{27}{100} \times \$3{,}000 = \$810$

20) Choice C is correct

$5 \times M + 4 = 5 \rightarrow 5 \times M = 5 - 4 = 1 \rightarrow M = \frac{1}{5}$

21) Choice E is correct

$\frac{42.6}{100} = 0.426$

22) Choice B is correct

The angles on a straight line add up to 180 degrees. Then: $x + 25 + y + 2x + y = 180$

Then, $3x + 2y = 180 - 25 \rightarrow 3(35) + 2y = 155, \rightarrow 2y = 155 - 105 = 50 \rightarrow y = 25$

23) Choice B is correct

let x be the number of gallons of water the container holds when it is full.

Then; $\frac{7}{24}x = 3.5 \rightarrow x = \frac{24 \times 3.5}{7} = 12$

24) Choice C is correct.

The ratio of lions to tigers is 5 to 3 at the zoo. Therefore, total number of lions and tigers must be divisible by 8. $5 + 3 = 8$, From the numbers provided, only 98 is not divisible by 8.

25) Choice A is correct

If x is greater than 18, then $\frac{1}{6}$ of x must be greater than: $\frac{1}{6} \times 18 = 3$.

www.EffortlessMath.com

... So Much More Online!

✓ FREE Math lessons

✓ More Math learning books!

✓ Mathematics Worksheets

✓ Online Math Tutors

Need a PDF version of this book?

Visit www.EffortlessMath.com

Visit www.EffortlessMath.com

for Online Math Practice

Made in the USA
Las Vegas, NV
07 November 2022